MATERNAL DEPENDENCY
AND SCHIZOPHRENIA

Maternal Dependency and Schizophrenia:

Mothers and Daughters in a Therapeutic Group

A Group-Analytic Study

Joseph Abrahams, M.D.
Edith Varon, M.A., M.S.

INTERNATIONAL UNIVERSITIES PRESS, INC.

New York   New York

ACKNOWLEDGMENT

The research for this book was done at St. Elizabeths Hospital, as part of the Group Psychotherapy Research Project. Funds necessary to carry out this project were supplied by the Veterans Administration under Contract No. VAm 22844. Dr. Florence Powdermaker was Responsible Investigator, 1947–1949.

ACKNOWLEDGMENTS

The writing of this report has led to views on the distant as well as immediate influences which helped shape it. Of the latter, the members of this therapeutic group take an important place in its initiation. The mothers assiduously sought therapy until the doctor paused and worked with them. Their persistence in attendance was remarkable. In this respect, as in many others, they are a remarkable group of people, and we thank them for setting the problems and contributing to whatever insights we have achieved.

Certainly these mothers were acting in accordance with the special mores of the St. Elizabeths Hospital community, where the study took place, in openly asking for further curative efforts from the doctor for their "incurable" daughters. This hospital has a long history of innovations in psychobiologic and therapeutic research under Dr. William Alanson White and now, Dr. Winfred Overholser. Dr. Overholser's quiet encouragement of the therapist was of inestimable help in his efforts at establishment of a group psychotherapy program at the hospital, of which this experiment was a part.

Dr. Florence Powdermaker has been an ever available source of help and encouragement in the conduct and reporting of this study; to her we give especial thanks. The funds for the observation and writeup were furnished by the Veterans Administration through the Veterans Administration Group Psychotherapy Research Project (under Contract No. VA in 2284). Dr. Jerome D. Frank, in his capacity first as Principal Assistant, then as Administrator of the Project, has given freely of his time and talents, and has furnished helpful advice with the manuscript.

6477

This work is a sort of engagement, successful, it is hoped, of psychiatry and sociology. The interpersonal aspect of the experimental design was derived chiefly through the teachings of Dr. Harry Stack Sullivan and other members of the Washington School of Psychiatry. We are grateful to Dr. Frieda Fromm-Reichmann for her encouragement during the course of the work and her helpful comments on reading the manuscript. Mrs. Gwendolyn A. Goldberg, social worker, also contributed helpful criticism.

Dr. Lloyd W. McCorkle, an old collaborator in group therapy of one of us (J.A.), has helped greatly with the development of the sociologic aspect of the experimental design. He contributed specifically to this work with painstaking readings of the manuscript in its several stages, for which we thank him.

Lastly, grateful mention is made of the secretaries, Miss Catherine Gray and Mrs. Edith McIntosh, who labored long over the material.

CONTENTS

PREFACE

Among the many-sided approaches to the problem of schizophrenia, this monograph opens up a new avenue. The paths are clearly described but they point toward several relatively unexplored areas. To my mind, the authors have made two outstanding contributions to the psychological exploration of schizophrenia. The first is a method of study. The idea of putting in one group a number of schizophrenic women and their deeply anxious mothers to study their relationships was an original and imaginative approach and its continuance required courage and devotion. The continuing story of the relationship between mother and daughter was lived out, so to speak, before the eyes of the doctor and observer rather than recited or recalled as a case history. The value of such observations is plain from the account of what took place between patients and their mothers, and the record of the relationship between them and the doctor shows that such research can be carried out by the therapist and observer only if there is the willingness to submit to the rigorous investigation of their own reactions and the self-discipline that this implies. This gives the data a third dimension that is unusual and the validity is enhanced thereby. It is the paradox of this type of psychological research that such subjectivity on the part of the researchers is a necessity for objectivity and understanding of the problems. Also the study of the exceedingly complicated masses of data collected is of necessity difficult and time-consuming and demands an objectivity and capacity for analysis and organization of material not ordinarily required.

Another point in the methodology used that needs emphasis is the recognition that this type of research can only be carried on, as for example astronomy is, through protocols which set up methods of observations and the deriving from these of hypotheses which can be tested. This is in contrast to the use of controls for research which in the study of the inter-actions of the human being is a snare and a delusion as far as scientific validity is concerned.

A second important contribution is the clarity with which the dependence of the mothers on the sickness of the daughters is shown. The need of the mothers to feel superior is attained at the cost of the low self-esteem, indeed, the abject dependence of the daughters, but the conflict is kept alive by the rebellion of the daughters and their assumption, at times, of superiority and omnipotence in order that they may have a sense of existence, no matter how occasional and distorted the striving for this may be. It is as if such a mother had so little sense of the self that she cannot relate as an adult to another adult, but clings to her husband as a dependent child and can only feel that she exists if her child remains completely de-pendent. Thus she gains some sense of "being." This is indi-cated by the acute anxiety and anger when the daughter does not conform to her mother's requirements—the mother then feels as if she had no existence. The authors speak of the daughters as the mothers' alter egos. One might guess that the mother needs to feel this because her own ego is too frail to exist alone.

The experience of reading this manuscript for one inter-ested in the field of schizophrenia and group therapy is re-warding not only for the knowledge gained and the vistas opened but for its insights into the nature of psychological re-search. It is hoped that this method of investigation will be used to study the role of the mothers with men patients and of the fathers with women as well as men patients.

Florence Powdermaker, M.D.

INTRODUCTION

This is a report of a group-psychotherapeutic experience which took place in the visiting room of a mental hospital, St. Elizabeths, in Washington, D.C. The group was composed of adolescent and young women, chronically ill with schizophrenia, and their visiting mothers. It differed from the usual visiting-room assemblage in that it visited as a group, with the doctor.

The idea of utilizing this opportunity for therapeutic investigation was in accord with the policy in the group psychotherapy program at St. Elizabeths Hospital, where this experiment took place, of bringing out the emotional potentialities of groupings natural and meaningful to the individual, patient and personnel.

Soon after its inception this investigation received help from the standpoint of scientific study when the Veterans Administration Group Psychotherapy Research Project agreed to assign a research psychiatric social worker (E.V.) to observe and record the sessions.

The experiment became an absorbing one, as the problems in therapeutic approach, management, and record keeping became more evident; and personal involvement of both the therapist and observer in the issues of the group brought differences relative to the data. Susceptibility of the therapist and observer to the disturbing influence of the group appeared, but was brought into proper perspective when professional visitors to the group seemed to be incapacitated by severe emotional reactions to some of the group situations.

As the sessions mounted the problems of the members as human beings became clearer. The dovetailing of the defenses of mother and daughter stood out in bold relief at the

11

same time as the group members seemed to find their places in this little "society." The group acquired its particular flavor, as all groups do. This one seemed to be living through a peculiar fragmentary drama of intense slavish dependence of the mothers on the daughters coupled with cold rejection by the daughters. This happened simultaneously with an extremely condescending, destructive superiority on the part of the mothers toward their daughters, which was acquiesced in by the daughters with demonstration of extremely low self-esteem and infantilism. The relationships of each mother to the other mothers and daughters were of similarly complex and contradictory nature. All showed marked reactions to the doctor and social worker, resembling those to the daughters in the depth of what seemed to be the most prominent characteristic, i.e., their abject dependency, and its correlate, their omnipotent superiority.

Accurate recording of the phenomena incident to this group became easier as patterns became more evident. The events of each session were hashed over thoroughly by therapist and observer immediately afterwards until consensus or definition of differences was arrived at. Both therapist and observer knew they had a bear by the tail, and that the surest way to lose grip on the reality of the situation was either to stick blindly to pet ideas or give in to the other worker without working through differences.

It had become obvious that this group experience would yield much data about the mother-daughter relationship in schizophrenia, the problems of treatment of relatives in the group setting, the interaction of the neurotic and psychotic, and about many problems in dynamics of groups. The question of how much actual therapy could be done with this group was another matter. By therapy was meant from the first psychoanalytically oriented psychotherapy, modified from the classical procedure to adapt it for work with psychotics and with groups.

In the course of the group a great deal was learned. The analysis by the authors of the records amassed over the period of two years has taken another two years. Another several years could be spent on them, with profit. In the presentation of this material, as in its gathering, especial pains have been taken to keep the records as close in text and meaning to the phenomena observed, in short, as operational as possible. The data were boiled down in a multiple-stage operation through a process of abstraction and extraction, fired by an argumentative curiosity as to what lay within and between these people, including the therapist, which manifested itself in the relationships present.

The report is organized accordingly. First, the intentions and approach of the doctor and observer to the forthcoming experience are outlined. The members are introduced in the living context of the group as it was experienced by the doctor and observer, with some data as gleaned from the records of the hospital. A long chapter on the course of the group, with a running commentary and summaries along the way, follows.

The development of the group is summarized and the travails of the mother-daughter pairs and the doctor in the group are examined more closely in the next chapter, and some lessons derived are presented. However, the latter function is chiefly that of the last chapter, in which the data and conclusions obtained from terminal interviews with the group members are correlated with those drawn from the group experience. Also in this chapter, inferences are drawn on the interpersonal process, past and immediate, between the mother and daughter. An actual session protocol, and discussion of the at present extremely limited literature on group psychotherapy with members of families are presented as appendices.

This essay into investigation and amelioration of the troubles of these mothers and daughters was, though difficult, rewarding in facts, ideas, and it is hoped, helpful insights. Both doctor and observer have, at times painfully, been helped in their awareness of themselves and their interpersonal relationships. It is hoped that this report will move others to attempt similarly framed experiments both for comparison and furtherance of our knowledge.

I

APPROACH TO THE INVESTIGATION

1. GENERAL

In this chapter, the approach to the investigation is outlined. Questions and methods brought to the experience, from the standpoint of therapy and research, are presented. Since this is a clinical report, there is only limited discussion of theoretical aspects of the material presented.

This group experience was conducted in the context of an expanding hospital-wide program of group psychotherapy. In the approach to the phenomena found in these groups, the conceptualization of a number of quite different schools of thought was found useful, each applying best to a particular level of social and psychological organization. In the extremely important preliminary survey of the institutional or social setting for group therapy, the pragmatic conceptual frame of reference of modern American sociologists (Cooley, Mead, Dewey, Park, Faris, Burgess), especially their social survey methodology, yielded applicable questions and bases for inquiry. Helpful concepts and ideas on locating and studying smaller social groups within the larger setting were derived from sociologists and psychiatrists, especially the former, who had done actual work in social and therapeutic change with groups.

Current notions relative to the behavior of the individual were not particularly helpful in the actual approach until, in the course of development of the groups, the inevitable individuation appeared. Then the interpersonal concepts of Sullivan seemed to be most applicable, with their emphasis on psychological relativism and configurational patterns. However, the further the process of individuation progressed, the more pertinent became Freudian constructs, especially as regards the psychology of the dependent individual.

The study of this visiting-room group could be expected to furnish data on each of the levels of inquiry, and in accordance with the various approaches noted. However, concentration on the aspects of the experience which could yield most readily to therapeutic intervention and which could most reasonably be expected to give coherent and reliable data was indicated.

A certain hierarchy of interests and questions was evolved. Since this group in the waiting room was of familially related members, the problems of members of a family, and in this case, that of the most understandably verbal and overtly committed members of the group, the mothers, were exposed to view.

This relative availability of the mothers to inquiry overshadowed other important aspects of the investigation; namely, the problems of the daughters, and the phenomena of group formation. However, some valid data were expected in both of those areas. Some ideas were expected on the interpersonal factors between mother and daughter which favored or hindered recovery in the daughter. Illumination could be expected on some issues in psychotherapy, especially those involved in the differences in the relationship formed with alienated (schizophrenic) and normal (asymptomatic or neurotic) individuals.

Relative to the group phenomena as such, there were the lines of inquiry present in all group work: the processes in formation of the group, its course of development, with its differentiation from other groups (especially the therapeutic group on the ward in which the patients lived), internal dynamics relative to needs and drives of its members, the appearance of specialized functions and roles unique to its needs and situation, and its codes and patterns of communication and usages.

2. METHODS IN APPROACH TO THERAPY

The analytic group psychotherapy employed here may be characterized as an amelioratively oriented investigation by the members of the group, guided by the therapist, of their difficulties in establishing relationships with others. In this process, the members' conscious and unconscious wishes and drives are discussed in the light of what is revealed through their functioning in the group. It operates in the context of a group dynamism,[1] through mechanisms similar if not identical with those present in the ego-analysis aspects of psychoanalysis of the individual.

The role and capacity of the therapist was modified from that of the privately practicing analyst by a number of factors. Previous experience at the hospital with patients and visitors had taught that this was of great importance in the experiment. Though as group therapist he had relinquished administrative responsibility, he inevitably dealt more with administrative aspects of relationships than did a private practitioner. In addition, there were differences in his relationship with the visitors and the hospitalized patients. These differences seemed to exist on two general levels:

[1] A group dynamism may be considered a psychological entity of two or more individuals related through their needs and drives.

This unit manifests a degree of differentiation from the group, specialization by individuals (special capacities, roles), a historical past, established patterns of usages, communication and social change. The therapeutic group establishes a pattern of participation, action and reaction, and development of issues which proceeds on its own momentum, regardless of the absence of individual members or the occasional visit of a transient newcomer. The feelings expressed by members, and the issues discussed, are in the context of the dynamic pattern of the group as a whole.

the social and personal. The patients were under administrative control in a situation in which their whole immediate life was governed and in which the state of alienation from others with its implications was institutionally confirmed. The familial visitors were, in a social sense, dependent on the doctor for help in one aspect of their living, i.e., their relationship with their relatives. This state of affairs had important implications for therapy. With the patients it meant a profound state of dependency could be resorted to as resistance; with the relatives, the limited actual responsibility of the doctor could be used to avoid recognition that they had any problems outside of influencing the patient to recovery, or getting the doctor to see it their way.

On the personal level, the therapeutic problem was estimated to be of even greater profundity. The psychotic individuals gave evidence of having long since passed through the stage of perturbation and conflict as to their ego participation with others, and of having established themselves in various capacities of alienation from their own dependent feelings and those of others. In this state they had no heart for re-experiencing the travail of many years back, and fought attempts to get them to do so. Meaningful relationship with these people meant for the therapist and others awakening of feelings relative to the most profoundly disturbing of all interpersonal issues, that of abandonment.

The mothers showed on initial contact much interest in maintenance of their social capacity and roles, and in alteration of others' alienated states. They displayed initiative, but in doing something to and for the other person. On the whole, in common with visiting relatives generally, they seemed to be blind to much of their participation with others, in areas of living which had to do with their own strivings.

The mothers and daughters all differed in their ways of participating with others on the issues important to them socially and personally. There was a range of overt behavior and attitudes of rather extreme sort; for example, in the initial question on making efforts to talk with the doctor. Several of the mothers and daughters were persistent and others were extremely resistive.

Obviously, a therapeutic approach to these groupings involved some active work in guiding the group and making significant contact with its highly disparate elements. However, as in previous group therapy, much of the initial work was involved in forming an estimate of the interpersonal situation as the initial minutes and hours of contact went by. This was done in good part through study by the doctor of the impact on him of the interpersonal phenomena in the group. This will be gone into in some detail in the section on the participation of the doctor in the group (see pp. 173–182).

The doctor first established some initial impressions and hypotheses as to the problem at hand through his previous contact with them and through the act of experiencing the responses of the group members (including himself) to his initial question to them of what they had on their minds. He then set about guiding the group members in a discussion designed to offer them an experience in living in which they would have an opportunity to find the answers to their questions.

Guidance of the group members in the initial phase of the experience proceeded on several levels at once for the individuals of the several groupings. In this case the guidance was of rather refractory individuals in several groupings into exploration of their resistance toward facing their problems in dependency in the group. This experience occurred in the individual and the group sense, with the mothers acting as members of a mother subgroup, and the daughters likewise as members of their own grouping. The mothers and daughters were hardly on speaking terms with one another, and needed active guidance in their individual contacts and arguments with one another as familial members and as members of the mother and daughter subgroups.

One of the levels of guidance in these areas of contact was the social or in this case, administrative one. The group was formed by the doctor on signal from the mothers that they wanted that service. It was the doctor's responsibility to make arrangements and acquaint the group with the procedures to be followed. The mothers and daughters called for different types of handling here. The former were on the whole prepared in initial action to accept the doctor's formulation of the situation, later coming out with their resistances. The latter offered open resistance from the first. This situation called for active guidance of the discussion. The doctor responded to the mothers' questions with data, which he utilized as leads for further inquiry in the group. He actively fostered and led group discussion, thereby running into the resistances of the mothers.

At the same time, he responded to the daughters' positions, chiefly through acknowledgment, on the problems raised by the mothers. He indicated he expected participation by the daughters in accordance with their capabilities on the issues which were appearing in the group.

It had been found in other groups at the hospital, especially those containing heterogeneous elements, that this active participation in helping the group to work was extremely important because of the marked tendency of the group to become anxious and regress. A socially as differentiated from an emotionally re-educative experience was considered necessary. In this the doctor taught ways of going about things in the group. He was here an authority, albeit one whose prerogatives related only to the issue at hand. However, he educated first and only later investigated the resistances to education. It was expected that as the group worked through some of its initial anxieties, the participation of the doctor as a therapist proper would be predominant. This involved guidance of the members of the group through experiences encompassing questions of dependency, and collaborative examination of their meaning to the members.

It became quite clear soon after the treatment was begun that the mothers and daughters were in an endless cycle of "mothering" by the mothers and obscure negativism by the daughters, with each in the struggle only partially aware of her own feelings, and referring chiefly to the feelings of the other. In regard to this, one of the problems seemed to be the opening of the avenues of communication, into inevitably painful and stormy aspects of their relationship, and guiding the communication into significant channels as they were revealed in the experience.

The therapeutic focus was on the mother-daughter relationship, and the feelings they had about one another. The presence of a group of people in a similar fix was considered desirable therapeutically, not so much because of the support derived therefrom but because it afforded indirect channels of communication of feeling between mother and daughter. It was clear from past experience in group psychotherapy that awareness in the individual of his feelings about a current need is heightened by his involvement in a group discussion where his ambivalences are brought out and deeply explored by contending factions in the group.

To this purpose, an aim in the therapy was to bring about discussion of the immediate behavior and needs of the mothers and daughters by the members of the group in as deep, pertinent, and consensual a manner as possible.

3. METHOD OF RESEARCH

A word about the Veterans Administration Group Psychotherapy Research Project is indicated at this point. It was organized to collect and collate data relative to the behavior of the participants in therapeutic groups of various kinds (neurotic and psychotic, clinic and hospital). The project embodied the collaborative efforts of some twenty-two psychiatrists, four clinical psychologists, and two psychiatric social workers. Working together, with the psychologists and social workers recording the therapy and discussing the phenomena observed to arrive at agreement, generally applicable modes were evolved of observing, recording and discussing what went on in the way of patterns of relationships and the ways in which they were brought about. Events were studied in their context, chiefly through the means of a running record, a relatively free-flowing description of the significant events taking place in the group situation. Few *a priori* limits were set to the type or amount of data obtained; the emphasis was on development of insights into what was happening.

The records were not verbatim, but the attempt was made to record what seemed to have most diagnostic significance or to be dynamically related to other events in the group. When several persons were talking at once, as occasionally happened (sometimes on different subjects), gaps in the record were unavoidable. Otherwise, the observer recorded consistently and the records preserved the main trends of what was going on. For fuller, detailed exposition on this score, and also for exposition of relationships to previous, current, and future research in group psychotherapy, the reader is referred to publications by other members of the Research Project.[2]

In this research the aim is to define in concrete, operational terms the patterns of relationship which became discernible, both during the course of the sessions, in the therapist-observer interviews immediately following the sessions, and in the close study of the records later on. This placed em-

---

[2] A bibliography of the publications of the members of the Veterans Administration Group Psychotherapy Project is found on p. 238.

phasis, in the approach to and recording of data, on the ego operations of the individuals in the group, including the doctor.

Since this group constituted an experiment in group therapy, which is itself a relatively new field, the method of using the records and analyzing the data had to be worked on as the group proceeded. The fullness of the records, which attempted to incorporate the behavior as well as the verbal content of the meetings, was intended to make them flexible and applicable to a variety of uses.

From the beginning, the therapist and observer followed every meeting with discussion about it, which lasted up to an hour. These discussions covered general impressions of the meetings, sociodynamics, the dynamics of individual patients, and the behavior of the patients on the ward and their participation in the large group of patients on the ward. They helped development of sensitivity to the trends of the group, in addition to clarifying what had been going on in particular instances.

Practical circumstances limited the amount of data that could be obtained outside of observation of the groups. In most of the groups studied by the Group Psychotherapy Research Project an evaluation of each group member was made before and after therapy on the basis of psychological tests, social work and psychiatric interviews. This greatly increased the possibility of evaluating what had been accomplished in the group and of learning what other influences were bearing on the situation. In the present experiment, we were limited to social work and psychiatric interviews conducted after the period of group observation had terminated.

Shortly after the beginning of the observations, the therapist and observer agreed on one main point in the progress of therapy for the discontinuance of observation: the establishment of consensual and meaningful communication between mothers and daughters. We felt that this could be recognized when the participation of one member of the group was obviously an appropriate, overt and understandable reaction to the emotional expression of the other as manifested in the meeting. Observations were actually discontinued not long after this point had clearly been reached, as funds for the observer were limited. Therapy, however, continued.

When observations had been ended, the observer and therapist studied the records independently over a considerable period of time, to formulate what had apparently gone on in the group and what could be written up to advantage. When the therapist and observer then got together to discuss their analyses of the records, there appeared a remarkable similarity in their conclusions and in the evidence which they had used as significant. This may be attributed in part to long association together, but only in part, because never before had the records been subjected to this type of analysis; much of the material discussed in this phase had never been discussed before. Differences were discussed, with modification of views and conclusions. It is considered that this process enhanced the validity of the report.

II

THE MEMBERS OF THE GROUP

1. Introduction

In this chapter the personalities of the members of the group are examined by comparing them with one another, according to the characteristic behavior shown in the beginning phase of the group. The purpose is to explore the part the individuals played in the initial group dynamism, and to provide a descriptive framework, for clarification of the events which will be described later, in "The Development of the Group." Formulation of the group dynamics as such will be found in "The Group Dynamism" pp. 140–151).

This examination will be done through correlating the personalities of the members of the group from two points of view:

(1) As mother-daughter pairs: The interest here is in delineation of the observable differences and similarities to cast light on the specific emotional problems of each as shown in the group.

(2) As members of the group: The interest here is in the correlation of the characteristic modes of behavior and communication of the members as they responded to the issues which came up in the group. This would give an indication of how deep and balanced a discussion could arise on the points at issue; it may perhaps be described as the evident communication potential of the group.

25

Some background data are furnished, obtained from the case history studies of the daughters and individual interviews with the mothers at the termination of the experiment. Though these data are of some interest and to some extent illuminating, the source for this work of what are considered valid data is the observed behavior in the group.

It should be noted that the historical data obtained vary in area of coverage and amount from case to case. This is chiefly due to the focus of the interviews and therapy, the immediate situation and the inaccessibility of some of the mothers short of direct questioning for informational purposes. In this regard, the paucity of data relative to the husbands in this study is of dynamic significance.

2. THE MOTHER-DAUGHTER PAIRS: BACKGROUND DATA AND BEHAVIORAL INTERRELATIONS

Mrs. High and Hilda[1]

Mrs. High was forty-eight years old, Hilda twenty-two, at the inception of the group. Mr. and Mrs. High's parents were immigrants. Mr. High was economically in the upper-middle class. Hilda, the third of three siblings, the only girl, was raised to a large extent by nurses. She was bright and precocious until a year old. Between the ages of one and two she began exhibiting many fears, especially a phobia for hair. She walked at twenty-six months, and showed extremely asocial behavior. Most of her life from age six was spent away from home in special schools and hospitals. She was diagnosed as having hebephrenic schizophrenia on admission to St. Elizabeths Hospital two years before inception of this study. The Rorschach revealed predominantly catatonic features, with extreme sexual fears. She had, in the course of her hospitalization, fourteen electroshock treatments.

---

[1] All names are fictitious, and all identifying features have been disguised. Religious and occupational identification have been given only when considered dynamically essential.

On the ward she generally was untidy, tore her clothing, and scratched her cheeks. Seclusive at times, she wandered absently about the ward, shouting nonsensically. In the patients' therapy group, she would likewise wander in and out of the group, or would sit in self-absorption, muttering or screeching to herself. After some months she would, in an affectless, yet forward manner ask the doctor who he was, and could he give her her "years back."

When Mrs. High took her daughter out for walks on the hospital grounds, Hilda seemed to be the one in control, calling the turn on the course to be followed, with her mother begging her not to run away, and placating her with candy and cookies.

In the group, Mrs. High at first expressed worshipful, dependent reliance on the doctor, but concentrated her attention on her daughter. She gave the impression of exhibiting conformity to accepted upper-middle class ways. At times she overtly made bids for the attention and approval of all. She looked on Hilda with concerned contempt when she was nonconforming, and beamed on her when she performed adequately. Toward the rest of the group she seemed to typify the actions of a politician, turning to the group for support, attempting to find and express the groundswell of opinion.

Hilda gave an impression of being the bad boy of the group. She sat blankfaced and indifferent, next to or quite distant from her mother. She was tall and thin, the latter mainly because of her meager appetite. When standing, she slouched, and with arms grasping her shoulders, pressed her breasts flat. She would sit down, to fold magazine pages, and tap on them, producing a loud, irritating noise. She would suddenly get up, and stalk with long, mannish strides from the room. At times dressed in a quite charming manner, looking almost like a model, she usually was slouchily and somewhat demonstratively clothed in a crumpled cotton dress which she tore into shreds when displeased by something happening in the group. From time to time she scratched herself along the cheeks, pulled somebody's hair, or struck her chest in self-reprimand.

Mother	Daughter
Conformed, to the extent of showing enthusiasm for other people's interests.	Deviated openly, and demonstratively displayed apathy. Her interest in conversation was always with some person other than those with whor talking.
Took the center of the stage about Hilda, not herself. Acted as if she were self-effacing.	Either withdrew wit planation or took the c the stage in a very viv manner, similar to mot about topics, however, of ple and events from years b
Was feminine in manner, with a somewhat aggressive, masculine voice. Let self be put upon.	Was masculine (tough tomboy) in manner, strode like a man, with a little girl's voice. Hit people when she disapproved of them.
Valued culture, books, music; pushed Hilda to show mother's kind of appreciation.	Used books for the purpose of rattling paper. Enjoyed hearing opera, but wouldn't sing with her very fine voice.
Tried to break the pattern of Hilda's annoying mannerisms.	Indifferently continued the mannerisms.
Thought of Hilda "night and day."	Thought of someone else all the time, when with mother, and watched out for her in between visits.

Mother	*Daughter*
Wore her gray hair gracefully.	Wanted her years back.
Challenged the doctor to do something about Hilda's deviant ways, while saying that she was in his hands. Was apparently unaffected by his replies, compulsively continuing her complaint.	Was demonstratively unaware of the proceedings in the group, but came out with behavior and statements indicating deep comprehension of the doctor's and others' statements.
Was doctor-centered in her behavior toward people in the group other than her daughter. Used the statements of others as a jumping-off place for cajoling attacks on her daughter.	Appeared to pay attention chiefly to other patients in the group, to whom she was sympathetic.
Appeared to like herself, preening and building her accomplishments and status prerogatives up to the doctor and others. Appeared quite helpless in the face of her daughter's deviant behavior.	Demonstratively did not like herself, and was the picture of inadequacy.
Spoke for the members of the group.	Spoke of people removed in time and place from the group. At times introduced all the members of the group to one another.

Mrs. High's defenses against anxiety in the group situation seemed to involve active demonstration of her cultural status and acceptance by society to the doctor and other mothers. Hilda seemed to have the initiative in the relationship. Mrs. High seemed to have her daughter as a constant point of reference, badgering and admonishing her when she did not employ her mother's defenses against anxiety. There were many similarities of behavior and other indications that the preoccupations of both were mutual. These appeared as issues, relative to interest in the right people, ambition, use of logic and reason, behavior appropriate to a respectable girl, the showing of feeling, responsibility for the current situation, and abandonment of one another.

Both mother and daughter exhibited their problems to the group, through their evocative behavior providing concrete examples, in their open semiargumentative struggle, of the problems in the mother-daughter relationship current at the time in the group. From the first, the reaction of distress of the mother to daughter's deviations was evident. It was extremely brief and resulted in a prolonged estrangement, in the initial phase of the group.

Mrs. Knowland and Karen

Mrs. Knowland was fifty-three years old, Karen twenty-six, at the inception of the group. Mrs. Knowland's father was a physician, extremely garrulous and dictatorial, and at times quite cold and aloof, who expected immediate compliance and great initiative in regard to educational matters. Her mother exemplified stoic martyrdom.

Karen was the third of four children, the first of two girls. Beautiful and adored from birth, she showed boldness, vivacity and "character" up to the age of seven. There was an episode of sex play with a small boy, for which Karen was banished to her grandmother. Throughout her life, the maternal grandmother was held up as a model to Karen by her mother. Karen was acknowledged by the family to take after her father in her ways, and her mother in her looks. Mrs. Knowland claimed she had rejected Karen as "too much for me," by being too harsh and exacting, with a growing rebelliousness on the part of the child expressed in offensive ways, like smearing the sheets with cold cream.

In her early teens, Karen had a period of "good" adjustment, but with the onset of her menses she became moody, was "tongue-tied" with boys and felt the other girls were talking about her. There was a struggle with her sister over a boy friend, with loss by the patient.

Karen finished high school, with steadily declining interest, and was hospitalized at several hospitals before coming to St. Elizabeths, over a period of ten years. Her diagnosis was hebephrenic schizophrenia on admission five years ago. At St. Elizabeths she became increasingly seclusive and dilapidated until the advent of the group treatment on the ward, when she began to show interest in the life about her sufficient to deflect her from the destruction of her clothing, masturbation and licking of her vaginal secretions.

In the ward therapeutic group she sat obediently, occasionally looking at the doctor with a derisive smile, muttering words like "potty," or some unintelligible, but definitive-sounding comment, which usually began with "I mean. . . ." Later, she began maliciously tweaking other patients' noses, while she laughed at the doctor.

When walking with her mother she was hunched over, appearing to be the dowdier and older one. They would walk together, and Karen would greedily stuff into her mouth the food her mother brought her.

In the mother-daughter group, Mrs. Knowland seemed to exemplify the smart, good teacher's pet. She frequently expressed intellectual defenses against Mrs. High's statements. While she listened to Mrs. High and kept Karen under her eye, she mostly looked at the doctor, and showed constant readiness to refute Mrs. High's statements. She expressed an accepted psychiatric viewpoint relative to the current issues in the group. This was done in a voice either affectless or unctuous. Later it became rasping. She kept a forced beaming smile.

She was able to verbalize, in her affectless way, on issues of deep significance to the mothers—on the problem of dominance and control and the underlying meaning of the daughter's behavior—intellectually crossing the group's emotional barriers to communication.

Karen, extremely plump, sat next to her mother. With a faint, Mona Lisa smile, she reached under her dress to her vagina, and licked the secretions from her hand. Her clothes were usually well kept and matronly, except for their edges, which she in moments of tension in the group disassembled thread by thread, placing them on her tongue and swallowing them. She scribbled notes on a pad and swallowed them after fairly thorough chewing. Her remarks were made in an unintelligible rush, with the use of vague, erudite words and mention also of fecal actions or the flushing of toilets. Later in the group's development she repeatedly drew pictures of faces with large round black mouths and eyes.

Mother	Daughter
Cultured, intellectual, beamed at others, especially the doctor, and spoke of others' ideas and interests, and "took in" their statements to her.	Used erudite tone to speak of fecal material. Occasionally smiled maliciously at the doctor. In a detached but lusty way masturbated and licked the secretions.
Spoke infrequently to her daughter, mostly to the doctor and Mrs. High.	Spoke in a clear manner only to her mother. Spoke mockingly to Mrs. High.
Acted as harmless as a church mouse. Remarked constantly on the others' domineering ways with their daughters.	Tweaked other patients' noses, tortured and pinched them, and acted masculine in seductive gestures toward other patients.

Mother	*Daughter*
Sat bolt upright, smiling benignly.	Slouched in a slothful manner; enigmatic and malicious smile.
Plain and matronly, faint air of Victorianism in her manners and dress. Lips were pursed and thin.	Plain and matronly. Manneristic, whirled, got up and sat down as if in a ritual.

Though Karen and Mrs. Knowland seemed to be more overtly disjunctive, in that they rarely spoke to or looked at one another, the issues here seemed to be similar to those present between Mrs. High and Hilda. Mother and daughter seemed to be concerned with propriety, kindness and consideration, and their converse, gross impropriety, sadism and open enjoyment of physical sensations. Mrs. Knowland seemed to pay most attention to the doctor and Mrs. High, speaking to them, most critically to the latter. Unlike Mrs. High, who seemed concerned about acceptance by others, Mrs. Knowland deviated openly from the group members' cohesiveness in the face of the doctor and criticized them, also utilizing the doctor's way of looking at things. Karen spoke mainly to Mrs. High, in a mocking manner.

There was little overt struggle between this pair, chiefly a quick look of distress, covered by a forced smile, on the part of Mrs. Knowland when Karen licked her vaginal secretions.

Mrs. Tenant and Tina

Mrs. Tenant was forty-seven years old, Tina twenty-two, at the inception of the group. Mrs. Tenant's parents were remarkable for the extremes of their characteristic attitudes. Her mother was a "saint on earth" who constantly looked after others' welfare. Her father, whom Mrs. Tenant strongly resembled, was a duty-bound person who had worked as an attendant at St. Elizabeths and whose motto was "death before dishonor," and "no compromise." The fifth of ten children, Mrs. Tenant rebelled against her parents' wishes by marrying outside the strongly held family religion.

Tina was the second of four siblings. "Normal and a beautiful baby," she had a severe attack of whooping cough at seven months. Following this she was retarded, and walked and talked at two and a half years. Her vocabulary from then on was extremely limited, and her speech like that of a one-and-a-half-year-old. Mrs. Tenant took care of Tina as if she were at that age from then on. Tina appeared to be quite aware of what others were saying and doing, but "couldn't express herself." Mother kept her near her all the time, devoting herself to her care. The other siblings seemed to grow and develop without untoward difficulty.

Tina was admitted to the hospital in 1945 because of prolonged screaming and self-destructiveness, taking the form of biting her forearm. Discharged after several months, she was readmitted in 1947 for the same complaints. She was diagnosed as having psychosis with mental deficiency. On the ward she was seclusive, and screamed in terror a great deal at night. At times she would be sexually seductive toward other patients. She spent much of her time looking at magazines. She showed some dilapidation of personal habits, but wore the little girl's clothing her mother dressed her in.

While with her mother out on walks, Tina would walk like a little tot, with her mother ministering to her needs, offering her goodies.

In the ward therapeutic group she made mocking, animal-like noises during most of the early sessions. Gradually these became more directly appropriate to the events in the group, and appeared to be related to the doctor's interest in other patients. Words like "che-cher" (teacher) became recognizable. Tina then began open sexual seduction of several passive and withdrawn, but highly intellectual patients.

In the mother-daughter group, mother and daughter invariably sat together, with mother in close physical proximity to daughter, either through pulling her head onto her lap, or through stroking her body while Tina was seated beside her. This contact did not seem to be the central point of interest for Mrs. Tenant, although she looked at Tina from time to time. For the most part, she watched the doctor and the group members intently, showing intense, open, unverbalized reactions of approval, disapproval, sadness, anger, etc. She denied awareness of and would not verbalize about others' acts and feelings, but was direct and forceful about her own: "I feel terrible lost without Tina." She dressed for the most part in matronly fashion but with a low neckline somewhat out of consonance with the predominant note of her attire.

Tina's facial expression in the beginning phase of the group was, for the most part, empty and feral. In a slow, pained contortion, chiefly centered about the lips, her eyes protruding in an empty stare, she verbalized barnyard sounds. At times she emitted a mocking laugh, and then looked at the person mocked in a very shy, distant manner. She was dressed usually in little girl's clothes, her hair in well-kept braids, which the attendant put on top of her head, and which her mother immediately would pull down and tie with a little girl's bow. Mother would then feed daughter candy and soda pop, and urge her to color crayon books—"to keep her happy."

Mother	*Daughter*
Held onto daughter and caressed her, looked occasionally at her tenderly or with despairing concern.	Received the caresses and attention passively and occasionally responded in kind, with blank eyes and animal-like expression on her face.
Watched others in the group intently with evident open, but unverbalized reaction of agree-	Much of the time apparently unaware of others besides her mother. Emitted barnyard

Mother	*Daughter*
ment or disagreement, defiance, or acceptance, etc.	sounds, which seemed directed at someone in the group. Looked at her own eyes in a pocket mirror provided by mother.
Protested despairingly that her daughter did not know anything, could not speak, and was hopeless, and cited numerous authorities to back her up.	Daughter was largely mute and appeared hopeless.
Asserted that daughter was completely innocent of sexual and other evil doing. Told of fear daughter might learn things from other patients.	Daughter at times made open, sexual love to other patients. Her laugh was quite malicious and mocking.
Dragged daughter down when daughter attempted to get up from mother's lap.	Either lay down compliantly, or got up, looked at the others and acted the epitome of childish surprise.
Mother at times whined in self-pity, appealing to others to pity her.	Daughter showed no open concern for herself.
Mother at times joined with Mrs. High, the mother who was most openly derogatory toward her daughter and the doctor.	At times on the ward waded into fights between other patients to spit on the one she did not like, then turned and bit herself.

The most marked feature of the relationship in the early group was the unwitting holding down of the daughter whenever she rose to pay attention to the others. Tina was apparently accepting of this blocking of even the postural inception of direct expression of feelings. However, she showed full and open display of hatred for others and self-hatred when open display of feelings took place on the ward.

Both mother and daughter gave evidence strongly suggestive of an early fixation in a mother-infant relationship. They evidenced preoccupation about the question of physical closeness, innocence, and expression of feelings about one another and others. Issues between them were handled on the most direct and elemental level. There was no detachment and communication through the intellect as manifested by Mrs. High and Hilda. Though there was insistence by Mrs. Tenant on Tina's adherence to social proprieties, Mrs. Tenant defended her own seductive and openly repressive and babying attitude toward Tina. There was concern for self, both disguised and expressed, as doing things only for the daughter's happiness.

Mrs. Tenant in her statements and manner of speaking seemed to be defending herself against expected accusation of wrongdoing against her daughter. Her direct babying relationship with her daughter brought out in bold relief that aspect of the problems of mother and daughter.

Mrs. Link and Laura

Mrs. Link was fifty-seven years old, Laura thirty-five. Mrs. Link's father was a charming but extremely sarcastic person who was "frantic about sex" (delinquency) on the part of Mrs. Link during her adolescence. Her mother was reported as a sweet, gentle soul. Mr. Link also was reportedly good natured and gentle. Since Laura's illness he took to heavy drinking of beer and direct and negative expression of his feelings. He apparently left the major part of the burden of raising the children and support of the family to his wife.

Laura was the first of three siblings, and was normal from birth to five years, when she stopped growing and the older of her two brothers began to outdistance her in growth.

She was a good-natured, well-liked child, who sang well, and showed good aptitude in spelling and arithmetic. She slept with her mother since childhood, the father sleeping in another room. She played with dolls until the age of seventeen, and played with small children until late in her teens. Menses began at the age of nineteen, with menorrhagia calling for transfusions. She stopped school at the first year of high school at this point.

Laura and her mother were extremely close prior to the onset of the schizophrenic illness at twenty-five. Laura was openly jealous of her father's friends and of the people Mrs. Link talked with over the phone.

The illness started gradually, with increasing irritability, accusation of her father of sexual designs on her, and of calling her a midget. She showed jealousy of her brothers, and was possessive of her brother's children's playthings. She complained of hallucinations of being called a midget.

She was hospitalized after an illness of seven years in 1946, at the age of thirty-two, and was diagnosed as having paranoid schizophrenia and polyglandular disturbance. On the ward she generally sat by herself all day, and gradually showed habit deterioration. In the patients' therapy group she was alert at first, smiling childishly. She then began to speak to the doctor suggestively of "goosy-gander" (probably referring to sexual relationship) as what was on her mind. She would at times spring up and strike the patient the doctor was talking with, later crying disconsolately.

When her mother took her for walks, she quarreled constantly, while her mother offered her food and crayon books, reiteratively affirming her affection for her daughter which Laura in turn denied. Laura would emphasize her mother's age and facial blemishes until her mother was in tears, at which time she would vow loyalty to her mother.

In the mother-daughter group, Laura would sit either

next to, or quite distant from her mother. She either stared blankly ahead or remonstrated actively with her mother, and with a pained, angry expression reprimanded her for what she had just said. At times she smiled winningly at one of the mothers, or flirtatiously at the doctor. She made pithy, sarcastic remarks when her mother urged her as usual to faith or action. At times, Mrs. Link would, in a whining and self-pitying manner, describe in great detail the latest difficulty she had had with Laura, thereby verbalizing a concrete and typical situation the other mothers could not broach.

Mother	*Daughter*
Spoke in a whine and with self-pity for daughter and self to the doctor, generally ignoring other members of the group.	Was either distant and aloof, or quite winning toward other mothers and seductive and kidding toward the doctor.
Whined about daughter doing things to her. "Told on" daughter in the group.	Angrily and imperiously told her mother to shut up.
Overwhelmed with concern for daughter's life.	Acted as if unconcerned, especially in regard to her small size.
When pleased was extremely impulsive and full of her pleasure to others.	Same as mother. Expressed hostile feelings quite directly by blows and kicks.
Showed bumbling ways in dealing with daughter.	Showed active and bright intelligence and awareness under façade of childish bumbling.
Stated that Laura was her "whole life."	Showed some jealousy, and a degree of spontaneity with others, but marked possessiveness with her mother.

There seemed to be a sort of lovers' quarrel here, with the mother complaining of the daughter's mistreatment of her and the daughter cynically bringing her mother to tears, then avowing her love. In relation to the group, Mrs. Link urged faith in the doctor which Laura rejected. The issues of sexuality, of who is dominant, of the age difference between mother and daughter, of social desirability, of physical appearance, etc., were present here in fairly open form, with Mrs. Link reassuring Laura and Laura testily rejecting her mother.

Mrs. Roper and Rae

Mrs. Roper was forty-three years old, Rae twenty-two, at the inception of this study. Rae's grandmother was a rather portly, goodhearted but bossy housewife and a quiet worrier. She paid especial attention to Rae, spoiling her, giving in to Rae when Mrs. Roper would not. Mrs. Roper: "That's why Rae loved her more than myself." Rae's grandfather was nervous, ebullient, ready to explode at anything that went wrong.

In her childhood, Mrs. Roper was very obedient, but at times extremely stubborn, "wouldn't give in, just like Rae. . . . I was nervous in the same way as my father, but I knew when to hold it in." She was extremely devoted and close to her parents, and was apparently popular with others of the same age. She graduated from high school with average grades, and worked competently as a stenographer in a government office.

She married at twenty-one, against her parents' wishes, who objected to the religion and poor earning capacity of her husband. Mr. Roper resembled Mrs. Roper in being "quite moral" and "too easy in some ways and stubborn in others." He was high strung and nervous. From the first there was intense conflict between Mrs. Roper and her husband over her adherence to the Catholic religion, with Mrs. Roper winning out on the side of devout adherence.

Five years after the marriage, Mrs. Roper resigned her

secretarial position to bear Rae. She had lived close by her parents all this time and her mother played a dominant role in Rae's upbringing. Mrs. Roper in addition attended a pediatric clinic regularly to "make sure" that what she was doing was right.

Rae's birth and early development seemed normal, except for a persistent tendency to have her own way, and "hotheadedness; if she didn't want to, she didn't." Rae was a beautiful child, popular and appealing. At the age of three she sang and danced on a public stage.

Her grandmother was extremely indulgent to Rae, and imperious toward Mrs. Roper relative to Rae's upbringing. Rae showed similar ways toward Mrs. Roper. Rae exhibited her mother's devotion to orderliness and cleanliness, but occasionally stubbornly refused to go along. "If I told her to do something, she wouldn't obey, or disobey, but do something in between, in her own good time."

Rae did well in her studies, was a fairly popular girl, but had only one close girl friend. She was frightened by the onset of her menses, but showed no persistence of her initial perturbation, after explanation of the process by her mother.

Her younger brother was born when she was eight. "She loved and bossed him . . . stood off and just looked at him . . . everything revolved around her anyway." Rae showed great and open devotion to her grandmother, much less to her mother. The grandmother died when Rae was fifteen years old. Rae remained with the coffin, "as if she were alive," for a long period. After that, Rae had to be pushed to go with other children.

The first serious open conflict with her mother came when, at the age of sixteen, she passionately wanted to accompany her girl friend to New York City to hear a romantic singer at a concert. Her mother forbade it on the grounds of the danger to her morals. After her friend went on with someone else, Rae showed toward her mother great and despairing recrimination.

On graduation from high school, she insisted on wearing an old, dowdy dress to her school play, and on remonstration by her mother, "if you wear that dress, I won't step out of this house," she tore up the tickets and left in a huff, without her parents. She refused to recognize them later in the evening.

After graduation at eighteen in 1943, she took a stenographer's job at a government bureau, and performed her work well. She gained weight up to 155 pounds, and engaged in intermittent and severe dieting and medication to bring it down. Her mother threw the medicine out and threatened the doctor prescribing it.

Rae was attracted to a young man who was "nervous and high strung," and went to his apartment after a drinking party at the office on Christmas. Her mother was incensed and intervened in the situation, driving the young man off.

Rae became more withdrawn, and had sudden apparently inappropriate outbursts of temper, in which she struck her mother. She would grab hold of her father and accuse him of trying to rape her. She played the phonograph a good part of the night, and again accused her father of trying to rape her when he remonstrated.

She was hospitalized at the age of nineteen, and was diagnosed as hebephrenic praecox. She received twenty-four electroshock treatments with only temporary improvement. She became increasingly dilapidated and negativistic, and refused to see her mother.

On the ward Rae would often stand at the window anxiously awaiting her mother, at times refusing to see her when she came. When she did see her she would demand to be taken home and then terminate the visit. She was untidy in her habits and dress. Generally seclusive, sitting with face in hands, she occasionally assaulted another patient without apparent provocation.

In the ward treatment group Rae at first was completely withdrawn, but soon would glance seductively at the doctor. She later sat next to him and attempted to caress him, telling him shyly that she liked him. When he spoke to her she would hide her face and cry. Occasionally she would pull the hair of some withdrawn patient. She would occasionally speak of home in a gleeful, childlike manner.

In the mother-daughter group Rae sat next to or quite distant from her mother, turning from her in annoyance when Mrs. Roper spoke to her. Mrs. Roper generally was a passive listener, following the lead of the more aggressive ones, especially Mrs. High, literally puffing up whenever one of the daughters rejected her mother.

Mother	*Daughter*
Smiled constantly, but showed quick and sudden nonverbal displeasure at other daughters' disobedience of their mothers.	Withdrawn, but showed sudden changes of mood, and expression of pleasure, anger, or tears, without verbalization.
Stated that her life was centered about Rae, and that she longed for death for the lack of her.	Showed anguished waiting for her mother's visit, then angrily or tearfully rebuffed her.
Was plump and matronly.	Was plump and matronly.
Echoed the dominant sentiments in the group.	Spoke only of her preoccupation.
Looked attentively at doctor, acted compliant. Was quite serious.	Covered face, showed disgust on face. Occasionally flashed an extremely seductive smile.

Both mother and daughter in the group seemed to be blocked in the expression of their feelings, the daughter less so. Both were impulsive and showed sudden mood swings.

They had mutual preoccupations about sexual propriety, their age difference, jealousy, and abandonment of each other.

Mrs. Springer and Sally

Mrs. Springer was forty-nine, Sally twenty-four, at the inception of the study. Both maternal and paternal sides of the family showed a great deal of concern with family traditions. Mrs. Springer's mother apparently was preoccupied with her own short stature and corpulence. Mrs. Springer's father was a professional man, charming, accomplished, and quite slender, who emphasized athletics and horsemanship, and who died when Mrs. Springer was six years of age. There were three children, all girls; Mrs. Springer was the youngest. Mrs. Springer had a brief psychotic episode in her early twenties when she was disappointed in a largely fantastic love affair. Her recovery was marked by intensive indulgence in health faddist activities. Mrs. Springer apparently carried these motifs into her marriage to a man similar to her father, but otherwise quite unreliable, and opposed to domestic ties. She starved herself during her first and only pregnancy to keep herself and the child thin, and after its birth attempted to keep it thin by keeping its feedings down. Mrs. Springer pushed Sally as a child into areas of cultural and athletic accomplishment. Her husband divorced her soon after Sally's birth, and the responsibility of raising the child was shared by Mrs. Springer and her two spinster sisters. The father "kidnapped" the daughter at two, but was thwarted in his efforts to raise the child, although Sally indicated her desire to live with his family.

Miss Sheppard, a sister older than Mrs. Springer by several years, differed from her in a number of ways indicative of an intense covert rivalry. While both emphasized physical beauty and performance, with strong overtones of self-improvement and superiority over those who did not do so, Miss Sheppard showed marked talent and careerist direction in the expressive arts. Mrs. Springer seemed to be more intellectually inclined, and was unsuccessful. Over the years, Miss Sheppard had sympathized and physically cared for Sally, unlike Mrs. Springer, supplying understanding explanations for Sally's untoward behavior, in contrast to her mother's condemning attitudes.

Sally was bright, gifted and tractable to her mother's and aunts' directions until the age of thirteen, when menstruation began. The issue of sexual expression was attended by intense preoccupation on that score by daughter and mother with increasing defiance through deviant behavior by daughter. Impulsive, odd, and destructive behavior when thwarted in the promiscuity which occurred resulted in hospitalization at the age of sixteen for three years, then at twenty-one until the present. Sally was diagnosed on admission as having a hebephrenic psychosis. On the ward she was seclusive and underwent a gradual habit deterioration. At times she would impulsively and apparently without provocation assault another patient, or screech obscenities at her. In the ward treatment group she was at first quite withdrawn, but in a few months engaged in cycles of dramatic seductiveness toward the doctor, disappointment, castigative assaultiveness, withdrawal, and then recurrence of the seductiveness, etc., with greater and more appropriate verbalization. She occasionally assaulted and threatened to bite other patients.

On walks with her mother she would walk with a severe slouch far ahead. Her cheeks would be brightly rouged, apparently in caricature of a prostitute. The mother, with a set and determined smile, would trail behind with a bag of goodies.

In the mother-daughter group, the two invariably sat next to one another. Mrs. Springer, with a beaming expression, would in a high-pitched, chirpy affectless voice address herself to the doctor, reiteratively advocating in the form of a question, sunbathing or dancing in the nude as an answer to the problem of the behavior of the patients. Toward the end of the observation period she would occasionally remark casually on the hopelessness of it all and her death wishes toward her daughter. Sally sat slouched, bored and distant. Her voice was deep and rich and she at times would utter, "I mean," or "Don't you remember?" suddenly halt, hold her mouth, and laugh in a despairing yet impish manner.

Mother	*Daughter*
Benignly looked at doctor most of the time, at times looked at daughter disapprovingly.	Sat slouched, cynical, sallow.
Quite feminine in dress, at times wore quite low necklines for the afternoon. Spoke careful, stereotyped "clean" language.	Wore slacks. Had a somewhat masculine cast to a well-formed face. Spoke in a pithy, neologistic and obscene manner.
Walked in a determined, vaguely spirited manner about a dozen paces behind her daughter.	Dragged her feet, but managed to keep ahead of her mother.
Spoke in a high-pitched, chirpy, affectless voice of the here and now, how it should be changed along health faddist lines, and how it was a pity to have all these unfortunates here. They were better off dead.	Spoke to the doctor in a deep, somewhat appealing, seductive voice, "Don't you remember?"

The mutual preoccupations seemed to be in the same areas as with the other mother-daughter pairs—sex, control, loyalties, recrimination, ways out of the conflict—with the struggle taking a highly dramatic cast, in many regards similar to the Highs. Seductiveness toward a male figure and death wishes took open expression, and contributed in the group interaction an aspect of the mother-daughter relationship of vital importance.

Mrs. Angell and Astrid

Mrs. Angell was thirty-nine, Astrid fifteen, at the inception of this study. Mrs. Angell's paternal grandmother watched closely over the family especially after her father died, when Mrs. Angell was seven. The grandmother was a hard-working, strict, "wonderful" woman. Mrs. Angell's father "was quiet, had wonderful morals and no bad habits." Mrs. Angell still grieved his death, "not quite over it." Mrs. Angell continuously strained after that to make her mother happy. Her mother was "very strict, with a bad temper, and I couldn't please her, and was afraid of her," though Mrs. Angell was a good cook and housekeeper from the age of nine. "I had the responsibility for the four children and not much of a childhood." When Mrs. Angell was twelve, her mother married a man thirteen years younger than herself who, though he was kind and pleasant, was unfaithful. When the latter quality became prominent, her mother would not speak to him, and then began nagging him, and became stricter with the children. Mrs. Angell's education was impeded by her duties and interest in the household. Though she could never talk interestingly, she could write a good letter.

Mrs. Angell, unhappy at home, eventually left to marry, against her family's wishes, a charming, sophisticated, selfish, independent, and ambitious man. He teased her a great deal but otherwise they were happy for a while. He lost interest in her, "he went all to pieces," as soon as she became pregnant. Mrs. Angell reported that she could not please him and, needing love, packed her suitcase and went home to her mother. Her husband never took her back. She almost miscarried, but the baby came to term. "I was so happy about that baby." Mrs. Angell waited for her first husband to return, and "lost control of myself to my mother." "He wouldn't speak to me, but after the baby came I never gave up hope he would love the baby."

Astrid was a breech baby, and was apparently quite normal in her early development. She was raised in her grandmother's house until the age of two, when her mother divorced and remarried. The maternal grandmother from the first treated Astrid as her child, and "helped Astrid to be impudent to me." The paternal grandmother "played up to Astrid, so I would lose control of her." The child was extremely appealing and bright, and showed her father's brilliant ways, deriding her mother. Mrs. Angell, in turn, was quick to admonish her daughter and punished her by refusing her privileges. Mrs. Angell remarried when Astrid was two and a half years old, and moved to a distant city. Her second husband was usually kindly and understanding, but at times was stern, quite alcoholic, and irritable, "awful when drunk, fussed and cursed, made the family unhappy and afraid, and Astrid the afraidest of all."

While living in a distant city, the family was relatively stable, and Astrid showed great sensitivity and appeal, and "was ahead of her time verbally, answering back with a mind of her own. You had to say things strict to get them done." Astrid would do things at her own pace in her own way. She made friends easily, and was usually the center of attraction. She did well in school. Though she competed with her two sisters, they were not quite in her favored position in the family.

A prominent activity in the Angell household was play-acting, where Mrs. Angell would, as a sort of fantasy ceremonial, recite and dance before her husband and children. The children would join what at times were sensually colored activities.

When Astrid was eleven years old, the family moved back to Washington, close by the maternal grandmother. Mr. Angell went on the road for long periods in his business and was more irritable. The domineering grandmother abetted Astrid's defiance of her mother, and told Astrid she had to be her protector. At the age of twelve, Astrid was informed by her paternal grandmother of her real father, in derogatory terms, of his "bad (German) blood, and his unsteadiness and bad habits." She became preoccupied, and spoke to her mother in bitter terms about the sexual ideas her mother forced on her. She became pubescent at this time, and extremely frightened by the appearance of menstrual blood. She showed tough boyish ways with the children at school, fighting them without provocation. She accused her mother of giving her only a small bust, large feet, and making her wear her dresses tight. (Mrs. Angell was well formed, and wore tight, high dresses, displaying her legs.) She accused her mother of poisoning her food, and identified herself with a vamp in a movie. She dressed like the vamp to go to school, and showed great concern about missing school because of a mild case of influenza, accompanied by apathy. She threw away presents given by a favorite uncle. There was constant mention of doing things for a boy friend. She claimed Mrs. Angell was not her mother and scratched her. Her increasing agitation resulted in hospitalization in June 1947, at the age of fourteen. She received fourteen electroshock treatments without improvement, and in two years showed periodic and increasing habit dilapidation, with a diagnosis of catatonic schizophrenia.

On the ward Astrid was mischievous, mercurial, imperious, and appealing toward the patients and personnel. She had periods of marked habit deterioration and infantilism. She entered actively into homosexual relationships with the more attractive patients. Much of her behavior seemed oriented around the theme of gaiety before disaster, with demonstrative sexuality.

In the ward treatment group, she often sat with her head in her hands, as if in profound despair, then suddenly, vivaciously and mockingly would call someone else "Astrid." She would accuse the others of obscene behavior and thoughts, and of being snooty, and then put her head in her hands, as if in grief. She would keep up a running commentary on the group discussion from this frame of reference.

With her mother on walks she would, with a distressed expression, demand obedience to her immediate wish. Her mother would apologetically placate her. Her dress would be appropriate for a fifteen-year-old, but her manner that of an old woman with an errant child.

In the mother-daughter group they generally sat very close together. Mrs. Angell was attentive to Astrid most of the time, placating her physically by attempts at caressing her, and through offer of things to eat. Mrs. Angell would at times ask the doctor what he thought she could do to make Astrid pay attention to the group proceedings, or complain about the way her daughter was mistreating her. At times she would offer information about Astrid's background. She would show little awareness of the doctor's reply, but would turn back to placating or remonstrating with Astrid, either in the manner of two adolescents quarreling in a movie, or of a very young child complaining to mother of mistreatment. This lack of difference between the two was highlighted by Astrid's calling her mother "Astrid." She seemed little aware at first of the existence of the other mothers although she liberally offered candy and fruit to the other daughters.

Mother	*Daughter*
Showed a concerned, troubled expression; compulsively and appealingly asked daughter to do things for her own good. Pitied her poor daughter.	Acted unconcerned, impulsively mischievous. Imperiously ordered mother around.
Dressed well, somewhat seductively, with pointing up of legs and breasts.	At times was well dressed, appropriate to her age. Mostly dressed in the most nondescript clothes, leaving her buttocks bare. Bemoaned her small bust.
Deferred to the doctor.	Ignored or was defiant of the doctor.
Provided data about Astrid's background, in addition to requests on how to control her.	Told about herself through speaking of another patient as Astrid.

The issues here were similar to those of the other mother-daughter pairs, with more open preoccupation with sexuality. On the surface, the daughter appeared to be the controlling one, but was blocked in expression appropriate to her age and relationship by mother's infantile appeals to her, and threat of abandoning her.

Ethnic background, reflecting considerations of status, played an important role. There was dramatic highlighting of the lack of ego differentiation between the pair, with sudden and startling switches in dominance and grandmother-mother-daughter identities. This served to highlight another especially important aspect of the mother-daughter relationship under examination in the group.

3. PERSONALITIES AND SOCIAL PATTERNS

Correlation of the characteristic ways of the members of the group revealed certain differences and similarities which were significant in the problems of therapy. They were gone into in detail at this point to familiarize the reader with this aspect of the approach to the group's dynamics. Mrs. Tenant and Mrs. Knowland seemed in the group to have diametrically opposite ways: Mrs. Knowland was highly intellectual, Mrs. Tenant almost entirely emotional: Mrs. Knowland permitted her daughter to deviate without intervention, and Mrs. Tenant stopped her daughter before she even began to; Mrs. Knowland had the ability to see both sides of the question by a philosophical mechanism of detachment, while Mrs. Tenant was immediately submerged by it; Mrs. Knowland was compliant to the doctor, while Mrs. Tenant was immediately but nonverbally defiant with full display of feeling; Mrs. Knowland disowned need for support from the others, while Mrs. Tenant directly appealed for it; Mrs. Knowland in an intellectual way was able to describe her anger, while Mrs. Tenant completely and immediately disowned it. However, Mrs. Tenant showed no other defenses against her anxieties, than direct cutting off from the other person or direct display of feeling.

The other mothers seemed to fall in place somewhere between these extremes, Mrs. Link showing Mrs. Tenant's self-pity, despondency, direct dependency on her daughter, yet some of Mrs. Knowland's ability to stand off and verbalize her feelings without actually feeling them. She also showed some of Mrs. Knowland's polite bossiness, in some contrast to Mrs. Tenant's protestation of "only knowing about Tina." This in-between position later in treatment made her valuable as a mediator between Mrs. Knowland's and Mrs. Tenant's ways of approaching their daughters.

Mrs. Angell's verbalized pity for her "poor, confused" daughter was similar to Mrs. Knowland's "understanding" of her daughter's misfortune of having had a mother like herself and of the right to feel resentful. Mrs. Angell expressed anguish similar to Mrs. Tenant's, but for her daughter. She intellectualized numerous reasons for the catastrophe in terms of family history, problems of adolescence, social conditions, with comparison of her daughter to many other girls with similar problems. This was in contrast to Mrs. Tenant's repeated protestation that her daughter was completely different, just as her own feelings were completely different from the other mothers' in their lack of hostile intent.

Mrs. High unceasingly attempted to change her daughter, nagging her to conform to the dominant modes of society, to Mrs. High's idealized image of herself, and to her own way of expressing hostility in a seeming on-the-surface, straightforward, righteous manner. This was halfway between the extremes of Mrs. Tenant's position of caring only about Tina and not caring for society, and Mrs. Knowland's enthusiasm for society as an abstraction. Mrs. High's aggressive and overriding seeking of the immediate approval and response of all in the group was in contrast to Mrs. Tenant's denial of interest in the group's and society's ideas.

Mrs. Tenant showed this denial through protesting that Tina was different. This was in contrast to Mrs. Knowland's mode of indictment of the mothers and herself for their domination of their daughters, in which she seemed unaware of the repercussions from the others. Mrs. High pitied herself and her daughter, and was able to express equally the despondency of Mrs. Tenant and the optimism of Mrs. Knowland.

Mrs. Springer was the closest of the mothers to Mrs. Knowland's intellectualized ways. However, she disowned her participation in the illness of her daughter, and blamed the hospital environment for its continuation, unlike Mrs. Knowland who blamed herself for it all. She was able on the other hand intellectually to verbalize feelings of rejection of the daughter and her own unfitness for motherhood. Mrs. Knowland's rigidly honest adherence to the intellectual view of things to be done was distorted in Mrs. Springer to a faddist one. She showed but disowned, as did Mrs. Knowland, overt dependence on her daughter for her own mood. Mrs. High asserted this dependence.

The daughters, compared on the basis of similarities and dissimilarities, fell into remarkable relationships to one another. Tina was opposite to Karen in many ways, but similar in others. Both showed recourse to direct bodily expression of tensions, Tina passively and without overt awareness of wrongdoing, being "loved" by mother and actively loving others. Karen masturbated and perversely ate all things available to her. Both laughed, Tina in a bestial and at times humanly mocking manner, and Karen in an empty but gay fashion. Tina adhered to her mother's ways, only occasionally departing from them to sit up and look around, and when away from her on the ward to attack the losing member of a fight and then bite herself. Karen completely deviated from her mother's values in her overt, perverse hedonism, and sadistically tortured other patients while she made love to them. Karen at times was bright-eyed, while Tina's eyes bulged blankly. Karen gave evidence of intense but detached intellectual activity while her feelings had perverse expression. Tina gave no evidence of intellectuality while her feelings seemed to have complete reign.

These marked and sharp opposites in ways were shared by the others in varying degrees. Sally had Karen's detached intellectuality, but occasionally burst forth in a rage or openly seductive episode. She voiced formed, poetically worded ideas on the topics of Karen's preoccupations (feces, death, lack of affection, despondency), but did so in a detached, passive speak-when-spoken-to manner, unlike Karen who apparently spoke only on her own initiative.

Hilda, as did her mother in relation to Mrs. Knowland and Mrs. Tenant, fitted somewhere between Karen and Tina.

She made a play for the group, and showed off her defiance. On the other hand, she showed that her mother's ways were her ways and struck herself when she misbehaved through actions or words. She verbalized about feeling, as did Sally, and occasionally and fleetingly showed it as did Laura. She berated her mother in a distant detached and mocking fashion, or made appealing gestures to her which brought temporary approval.

Astrid, who appeared later in the group, showed Hilda's and Laura's characteristics in exceedingly vivid and kaleidoscopic fashion. She did not make as persistent a play for the group's attention and approval, but was more commanding of her mother's solicitude. Her statements of low self-esteem were frequent, clear, and exceedingly self-derogatory, unlike Hilda's which showed obscurely as a beating of the chest or self-mutilation. Problems relative to racial and authoritarian hierarchy gained verbalized expression in a highly dramatized fashion. Astrid's show of feelings was more open, like Laura's or Tina's.

Laura expressed sarcasm and cynicism toward her mother, in which behavior she resembled Karen, but could express it in feeling ways. She was concerned chiefly with her immediate self, unlike Hilda, who seemed concerned about the responses of others. While taking food and other things to herself seemed to be important, she did so without ulterior purpose of reprisal or contempt for the prescriber of the activity; i.e., seduction, masturbation, etc., were more natural to her, as to a "child of nature." She wore little girl's clothes and had the manner of a child like Tina, but gave evidence of intellectualism like Karen.

Rae was closest to Tina in her childish manner, glee and seductiveness, and in her vacant pouting. She cried profusely when disappointed and either was completely acceptant of her mother as the only one she responded to at the moment, or completely rejective of her.

All of the mothers shared a common quality—of persistently maintaining contact with their daughters over a number of years. In this they differed from the parents of the other patients of this ward group. All of the daughters, likewise, in consenting to visit with them showed a degree of willing reciprocation. The contact made with one another ranged from the most intellectual to the most primitive on the part of the mothers, and was reciprocated by the daughters in obverse or markedly similar form.

In regard to any one issue about which all were anxious —say, daughter rejects mother—there was evident a wide range of potential communication on the part of the mothers and daughters. When realized verbally this resulted in illumination of the problem from the standpoint of the most rigid defenses of distance and the most openly anxiety-ridden needs for tenderness and care. On the basis of this aspect of the group dynamism, a problem of treatment consisted in guiding the group to the point where the group could admit the words and feelings of its members to its awareness and integrate it in its living.

III

THE DEVELOPMENT OF THE GROUP

1. INTRODUCTION

This chapter contains data necessary for understanding what happened in the group experience, and the steps by which communication and individuation developed. These data are presented in abstracts of the group sessions, as they occurred weekly for an hour for two years. As the group did, the data proceed from fragmentation, disconnection, and obscurity to much greater clarity, continuity, and meaning.

The data are accompanied by a running commentary on the individual and group dynamics, the process of communication, the way issues developed, were joined, and to some extent, resolved. The commentary is kept separate from the session abstracts, for the most part. In the presentation of the material the authors have taken the liberty of omitting abstracts of meetings which were of less dynamic importance. Also, as the therapy proceeded, and especially on review of the records, phases in the development of the group, marked by new modes of participation, were discerned. General comments presaging these phases are inserted to give the running text more meaning. The reader who prefers an overall synopsis and more coherent formulation of individual and group dynamics before starting on the details is referred to the next chapter, summarizing the group experience.

The participation of the doctor in the group process is

followed in this section. However, it is considered in greater detail, and from the standpoints of his emotional involvement and of the problems in therapeutic management, in Chapter IV, Section 5, on "Participation of the Doctor and Observer."

The development of the group was affected by a complex of interrelated phenomena: the individual dynamics of each individual member, and her reaction in the group situation; the relationship between each mother-daughter pair, which determined their behavior toward one another in the group and consequently modified their behavior toward the group, and vice versa; the relationships among group members which normally develop and influence them to explore and modify their attitudes in the group. Beyond this was the role of the doctor, who here constantly tried to move group members toward understanding and toward open expression of thoughts and feelings.

Several or all of these factors would be present as determinants of specific group events, making a thorough analysis of the group impossibly complicated and cumbersome. To single out any one factor for systematic comment would markedly distort the picture. Therefore, no attempt has been made to be complete with reference to any of the factors at work. Attention has been called to and interpretation made of some of the more significant events in the group whether they involve one or another of these factors.

As the group unfolded, the nature of the mother-daughter relationship first became clearer, then underwent some modification. These changes were related to the progress of the group. Particularly since the deepened understanding of the parental relationship was one of the most significant outcomes of this experiment, the commentary tended to be directed toward bringing out the dynamics of this relationship as they emerged in the group.

2. The Initial Situation in the Group

On initiation of the group the previously obscure maneuvering for position with regard to the doctor suddenly became overt and under the scrutiny of the group. Likewise, in the group session, the doctor was face to face with these importunate and repetitive mothers. The usual administrative techniques of avoidance through preoccupation with other duties, patient and noncommittal listening, or the offer of encouragement and reassurance became ineffective.

Changes appeared with the very inception of the group, and continued until termination of observation. From the first, members of this largely preformed group were brought face to face with one another on the issues which brought them to the hospital as visitors and patients. For the mothers, their previously rather casual and sociable association on the bus to the hospital and in the building during visiting hours took on a more sober and tense cast.

The original group was composed of Mrs. Tenant and Tina, Mrs. High and Hilda, Mrs. Knowland and Karen, and Mrs. Link and Laura. This group met weekly, rather faithfully. It was joined from time to time by mother-daughter pairs and by patients from the ward, at their request, for single sessions. Mrs. Roper and Rae joined at meeting 34, Mrs. Springer and Sally began attending in meeting 42, and Mrs. Angell and Astrid joined in meeting 52 and a sister of Mrs. Springer, Miss Sheppard, in meeting 45, attending from time to time. Mrs. High's attendance became irregular after the death of her husband, when she moved to a distant city.

These mothers were acquainted with one another through years of riding the bus to the hospital, walking the grounds, and sharing the waiting room when visiting their daughters. Despite this extensive and in a sense close contact, they showed for all their familiarity, great interpersonal distance, joining chiefly through communication of stereotyped and philosophically couched wishes for understanding and the recovery of their daughters. In the session, they spoke to one another chiefly through the doctor. They seemed to be quite unaware of the impact of their relationship with their daughters on the others in the group. They exhibited, in relation to their daughters, open, unabashed seduction (Mrs. Tenant), vindictive domineering (Mrs. High), querulous adherence (Mrs. Link), and distant, pained, hyperattentive non-intervention (Mrs. Knowland). The daughters showed, for their part, a distant, silent similarity of countenance, a blank face, broken by a mocking smile or laugh, or a disowned statement, or gesture. These things were a sort of dynamic counterbalance to the mothers' intensely emotional involvement.

The mothers hovered over their daughters and tended to withdraw their attention from the discussion current in the group setting at the slightest word or action from them. When Laura, in meeting 1, spoke of lacking faith in doctors during a general discussion of the patients' fear of disappointment, Mrs. Link turned her entire attention to Laura, admonishing her that she must have faith to get well.

The struggle about the attentiveness of the mother toward the daughter was apparently, as later learned, present in the family between the husband and the wife, and the other children and the mother. In the group the mothers were in conflict with the other mothers over it. In the course of the experiment the hospital personnel constantly attempted to point out to the mothers and the doctor what appeared to them as the too close attachment of the mothers to the daughters.

Despite the close attachment between mothers and daughters, one had the impression of two groups meeting simultaneously, one of neurotic women and another of schizophrenic women. The two groups were hardly on speaking terms, as individuals or as groups. It was characteristic of both groups at this point to relate primarily to the doctor, although Mrs. Knowland did talk frequently to Mrs. High. The daughters too participated singly and spasmodically for the most part, talking mostly to the doctor. Whereas the mothers occasionally got together in a general discussion in which they shared similar feelings of guilt, anguish or despair, the daughters on occasion joined together in laughing at some mother who had been made to feel uncomfortable.

From the very first the doctor participated in the struggle. He treated the daughters respectfully, and implicitly kept the issue of the mothers' disrespect alive. While attentive to the patients' behavior and interpersonal distance, he paid most attention to the mothers' demands on the daughters. In the communication on the problem of what was wrong between mother and daughter, he early took a stand about mother's part as restrictive and dominating; others (personnel, relatives) had taken the same stand in nonverbalized form. (See "Participation of the Doctor and Observer," on p. 173.)

Introductory Phase (Sessions 1–3)

During this period, lasting approximately three sessions, the sort of situations presented in the preceding chapter were experienced. As a phase, it really started when the doctor decided that, instead of answering the questions of the mothers as he passed by the waiting room, he would work on the mother-daughter relationship, and this decision altered his replies to the questions. It called for collaboration on their part, for which the group setting was indicated.

These three sessions were marked by a restatement by the mothers of their previous questions to the doctor. However, tensions and issues between the group members, including the doctor, which carried clues to the answers, made their appearance. In addition the abilities of twelve individuals, the mothers and daughters composing the group, were mobilized by the doctor toward arriving at answers. The tensions appeared as soon as the doctor posed the idea of looking at the relationships present in the group; until then the members had been going through their accustomed ways.

On the doctor's intervention, the situation began to evolve into areas of extremely dependent demands and reaction formations against them, in regard to the doctor and other group members. One mother began insisting on answers from the doctor, another supplying them, others claiming ignorance or confusion.

Session 1

The doctor stated that the group was called together in an attempt to look into questions asked of him and other doctors by the mothers and the patients through looking into what was happening between the mothers and daughters. He explained that both mother and daughter were asked to attend because he had seen them together so often in the visiting room at this very time, and also because it seemed appropriate to have whatever people were involved in the question to speak for themselves. There was some discussion of times of meeting, and expression of enthusiasm by Mrs. High, Knowland, and Roper for the idea of finding out what the trouble was, why the daughters were sick, and what the sickness was all about.

This opening statement and initial reaction were followed by a short but deep silence. Hilda began rattling a piece of paper. Mrs. High, with exasperation and challenge, asked, "How can I stop Hilda from doing that?" The people in the room turned to the doctor. He replied: "First let us look at what it means; what is she trying to do?"

Mrs. High spoke of the rattling as of unknown origin, and went on at length to tell of Hilda's detachment, of a deficiency of a chemical as the cause of Hilda's sickness, of her own despair in regard to getting anywhere.

Mrs. Knowland broke in at this point to ask if the group could read anything that would be helpful. The doctor asked if she had read much and when she enumerated books and publications, he pointed out that though it was perfectly good reading it apparently had not changed things much, and perhaps it would help to study what the trouble was right here in the meeting. Mrs. Knowland smiled, and sat back.

Mrs. Tenant spoke up about her Tina, to the effect that she could see no hope for Tina here, and besides, Tina was so different. Hilda made noise again, and Karen muttered.

Mrs. Link stated she never gave up hope, and "we had to look to the doctors for help, and not give up our trust in them." Mrs. High affirmed her trust in the doctors, and reiterated her question as to what should be done about Hilda's deviant behavior. The group became silent, and the doctor stated that this was a good question but that perhaps first we should go into what Hilda was doing to Mrs. High and Mrs. High to Hilda in their repeated interchange.

The next two sessions followed essentially this pattern, with the initial posing of a problem, such as what should be done to the daughter to make her well, response of the doctor calling for investigation and exposition, protest by the mother who began the interchange, communication of a doctor-oriented view by another mother, then prolonged and obscure expression by mothers and daughters. It was in the increasing clarity and pertinency of the communication and the commitment of the participants that the group dynamism developed its therapeutic effectiveness. In this process, the doctor focused on the immediate interpersonal relationships, gradually bringing out comment on the mother-daughter relationships most patent at the time, that of the Links and the Highs.

3. Appearance of Interrelations (*Session 4*)

In this phase, many of the mutual preoccupations manifested in the discussions as issues, modes of communication, and of relationship became recognizable. The issues in the group seemed to revolve about the problem of who was in control, or dominant in the situation. Problems in control were fought in relation to concepts of mother and daughter as to sexuality; social propriety; interest; initiative and ambition; pertinency to current reality; use of reason and logic; physical attractiveness; sociability; responsiveness; rivalry for the male in the family; unquestioning acceptance (faith); and display of tenderness and affection. Mother and daughter variously demanded compliance of the other on these points. Nonadherence or responsiveness seemed to result in subjective states of abandonment and despair, or anticipatory abandonment and negation of the other's significance. One or the other, in submitting, would display what seemed to be regression to earlier modes of relationship. In the case of the Links, and later the Angells, this was evident in the mother's childish manner of submitting to an imperious and domineering daughter. Mrs. High and Mrs. Knowland apparently helplessly surrendered initiative to Hilda and Karen, but maintained more socially adult modes of relationship to others.

Maintenance of dominance or control in the situation seemed to enable the mother or daughter to remain anxiety-free at the moment, and loss of control in the group situation resulted in actions indicative of profound despair, hostility, and sense of abandonment, with regression by the mother and assumption of more adult ways by the daughter.

The issues between mother and daughter were present and talked about in nearly every session, and expression of them became clearer and was accompanied by progressively more appropriate feeling. Each new session brought some variation in the expression of most of the issues, through some slightly altered pattern of relationships and communication.

A focal situation which had developed in the first three sessions was the "mothering" existent between the Highs. The doctor reacted and committed himself emotionally; and in the living through and surviving of this experience in the group, the group made its first therapeutic gain toward grappling with the emotional issues it faced. Mrs. Knowland and Mrs. High then committed themselves emotionally on the issues present, and significant cross-communication appeared. Also, in this session, differences between a mother and daughter (the Links) appeared. The introductory patterns of relationship had been altered.

Session 4

The doctor opened the session by reviewing the past three sessions, stating that expression of feeling had apparently done no harm, and some good, and asking, "What have we got to say today?" The mothers spoke of evidences of improvement in their daughters and the need for understanding them, and their hope that the daughters would tell what they thought of mother. Karen muttered about the answers being in the book. Mrs. High began by criticizing Hilda's rattling of paper, and Mrs. Knowland mentioned Karen's manneristic retracing of steps. The doctor with some irritation at Mrs. High called for investigation of the immediate situation between mother and daughter for the answers.

Mrs. Tenant in reply announced categorically that Tina did not understand what was happening. Mrs. High, with some irritation, protested that the mothers' protectiveness was benevolent. She then turned on Hilda's behavior as childish. Mrs. Knowland stated that it was "Momism" and that " 'Momism' was terrible."

Mrs. Tenant gave as proof that she was not dominating, "Tina's not being against me," and daughter's sadness when mother leaves her. Mrs. Tenant stated that she had been studying the problem for twenty years. Karen and Tina muttered. Hilda stated she liked Tina's braids and Tina looked pleased.

Mrs. High again asked if Hilda's problem was from something chemically wrong with her brain. The doctor asked for study of her daughter as a person and returned the discussion to the question of mothering and domination, and the mother's reaction when daughter strays. Mrs. High became defensive, and protested she was trying to help Hilda. Hilda mockingly said, "Goodbye, Mother," and left.

Mrs. Knowland blamed the illness on the pressures of society, as all mothers are anxious and vindictive. Mrs. High blamed Hilda's lack of incentive on association with other patients. Mrs. Knowland defended Hilda's lack of interest in the meeting as a gesture of independence, and pointed out that Hilda was listening intently.

Laura vaguely muttered, "Meat cleavers." Tension mounted, and Mrs. Tenant and Tina embraced, as Mrs. Tenant's face showed defiance of the doctor. Mrs. Link urged faith in the doctor on Laura.

Mrs. High attacked Hilda as fantasying, and told of her own need to "break this down." Mrs. Knowland defended Hilda. Laura defied the doctor and distressed her mother in stating, "No faith in doctors."

In this session, after the initial rendering to the doctor his due in good intentions and progress reports, the members went on to their growing controversy about the daughters' wrongdoing. The issue was joined on Mrs. High's reaction to Hilda's deviation through the abstinence of the doctor from social support of Mrs. High, revelation of his ego reactions to her, and guidance of the discussion toward dealing with interpersonal issues. Mrs. Tenant significantly turned to her daughter, this time not with "mothering" gestures, but through the explicit denial of daughter's comprehension of the situation, as a screen for her own blocked ability to comprehend. The intent underlying the "mothering" was revealed further by Mrs. High in her protest that the mothers were trying to help the daughters, in which she attempted to speak for the other mothers and implicitly sought their support.

Thereupon ensued Hilda's abandonment of mother, Mrs. Knowland's verbalization of the mothers' anxiety and vindictiveness, and her defense of Hilda. Mrs. Knowland was against Mrs. High in a bid for the group's support. The doctor had already committed himself on Mrs. High's behavior as in effect dominating.

The underlying tension in the group at the moment was voiced by Laura with her "meat cleavers" statement, and Mrs. Tenant reaching for her daughter as she looked defiantly at the doctor. At about the same time, Mrs. Link and Mrs. High showed their defenses against anxiety by turning to their daughters with exhortation and threats respectively. Laura came through with her clear protest.

The interactions between the mothers and daughters were similar to those before the initiation of treatment, with the exception of those of the Highs and Links. Here Hilda clearly abandoned her mother at the point where she was deeply involved with members of the group. Laura turned on her mother and the doctor, leaving mother visibly moved.

In the session movement was made in analysis of the process of "mothering" as a means the mothers used to control their own dependent feelings through maintaining socially sanctioned control of the interpersonal situation.

4. Appearance of Mothers' Feelings About Focal Issues (*Sessions 5–16*)

This phase, as they all do, dovetailed with the one previously defined. The relationships between the mothers developed to the point where, in a sort of showdown between one of the mother-daughter pairs, the Highs, in a rather tense scene, other mothers took sides with the daughter. More open rivalry developed between Mrs. High and Mrs. Knowland for the doctor's and for the daughter's attention and approval.

Feelings of despair on the part of the mothers, related to the daughters, appeared. The daughters began putting more feeling into their acting-out, presaging the next phase.

Session 5

In this session, Mrs. High recited in a patronizing manner new evidences of Hilda's consideration for her. Hilda, in an over-dutiful manner, stated to her mother that she was getting well. This was followed, however, by a protestation by Hilda in a colloquy with the doctor that she "doesn't live with others," and "through too much correction needs to run away." Anxiety became evident from then on, with Mrs. High complaining of Hilda's obtuseness and lack of ambition. Karen looked at her mother's book, *Love Against Hate*, scribbled little notes, swallowed the paper, and muttered comments about the meeting. The doctor encouraged discussion in the group of ambition in the daughters from the standpoint of what happens when the daughter does not have the requisite ambition.

Mrs. High demanded the proper response from Hilda. When none was forthcoming, she angrily asked to be embarrassed by accusations such as those of the past where Hilda accused her of putting her in school to get rid of her. Mrs. Knowland defended Hilda's immediate feeling as one of futility. Several of the mothers expressed a sense of discouragement and futility, with Mrs. High in tears and Mrs. Tenant supporting her.

In this session, Hilda complied mockingly but used the colloquy with the doctor to reprimand her mother, with words of abandonment. Mrs. High's defense of attention to Hilda's asocial ways became prominent, thereby avoiding her own dependent reactions; and when no support was forthcoming, she masochistically asked for recrimination from Hilda. Karen joined the interaction and, as in session 4, gave (as mother usually did, but in her own schizophrenic way) generalized comments about the meeting, this time perhaps pertinent to the problem of the Highs. The doctor intervened here to provide a bridge for discussion away from the impasse and fragmentation that was developing.

Mrs. Knowland supported Hilda, and Mrs. Tenant supported Mrs. High, both making movement in identifying themselves with a dissociated aspect of their personality. The crescendo of expression of feeling by Mrs. High set the pattern for the meetings to come for a long time. While there was little expressed feeling in Hilda's rejection of her mother, the verbalization was a commitment on an issue on which she had been nonexpressive. Each person in this situation seemed to switch to participating like or identifying with her opposite member in the mother-daughter pair.

The sequence between the Highs was one of estranged dependency, abandonment of mother by daughter, intensification of attentiveness by Mrs. High on aspects of Hilda's personality important to Mrs. High's defenses, masochistic request for recriminative attack from Hilda, and then despair.

The issue was at first on compliance to mother's defenses of social conformity, and then changed to that of abandonment. Mrs. High unsuccessfully attempted to switch it back to that of interest and ambition, but Hilda's withdrawal brought it out in the open, with the appearance of despair on the part of the mothers. Mrs. Knowland, through her attentiveness to someone else's daughter, made a step toward her own underlying sense of futility.

Session 6

Mrs. Tenant and Mrs. High commented on their daughters as homesick, disturbed and unreasonable. Mrs. High attacked the doctor as not logical, an attack similar to those she had made on Hilda. Tension became higher as Karen attacked Mrs. High as a "devil" and compliance as "potty." Hilda cried in an anguished way, "I don't want to work." She called for EST (electroshock) rather than the, to her, "enema" treatments of psychotherapy. Laura expressed resentment on being in the hospital, and her preference for her brother.

Mrs. High "appreciated" Karen's designation of her as a devil. Hilda laid her head briefly in her mother's lap. There was relaxation of tension as the mothers spoke of their daughters' improvement.

There was further development of communication between mothers and their daughters and cross-communication between Mrs. High and Karen. Mrs. High's attack on the doctor, presumptively a transference phenomenon, was the first verbalized one by a mother, and presaged freer display of feelings.

Significant also was Hilda's call for electroshock rather than psychotherapy, which she couched in anal terms. The issues between mother and daughter were further elucidated with Laura's extension of Mrs. High's mention of Hilda's hospitalization in the last meeting to resentment of her own hospitalization. Hilda showed warmth toward her mother when Mrs. High spoke appreciatively to Karen, in contrast to her "Goodbye, Mother," of several sessions back, when Mrs. High was engrossed in talking with group members, and emotionally on the defensive.

Session 7

The mothers' concept of daughter as a little child, "always seemed an infant," was brought up by Mrs. Tenant, the most overtly childlike mother. This was in defense of her insistence on Tina's wearing her hair down in braids. This gradually evolved into a consensus between the mothers on the need of the mother to keep daughter satisfied, "for fear of her tantrums" (Mrs. Tenant). Hilda spoke of cats scratching, and Karen of "they don't give you any affection, something really luscious. . . . you know the answers, only flush the answers."

Satisfaction was shown by Mrs. Knowland and Mrs. High when their daughters came out with appropriate and cutting remarks about the other's mother: Hilda's reference to Mrs. Knowland as "too wishy washy"; Karen, about Mrs. High's "hysterical patting around." Mrs. High expressed appreciation of Karen's expression "not giving a damn."

As the sessions went on the image grew of the daughter as someone mother placated, when conforming, and vilified and abandoned when nonconforming, and who had been a little child to mother all her life. The issue of mothering was prominent, with Hilda's and Karen's attacks on this score accepted on an intellectual level by Mrs. High and Mrs. Knowland, paving the way later for more emotionally meaningful communication.

Session 8

Mrs. High began by stating that she understood Hilda's need to act up and speak of other people all the time. (Hilda reiteratively mentioned the names of various people she knew in the present and past, including her brother.) However, she believed Hilda needed her to push her to conform. Alice (a patient on the ward who had requested to visit this group) and Karen laughed at Mrs. High in a way that deflated her.

Alice led off on a discussion of the daughters' fears of and need for the hospital. Hilda and Karen rejected the glowing picture of home presented to them by their mothers. This led to details in Alice's home life in which she stated her family depended on her and that her psychosis began when her father gave in completely to her.

The mothers then discussed their "natural" dependence on their daughters to get well. Mrs. Knowland asserted, in contradiction to Mrs. High, that it was the mother's responsibility. There was gradual and vague revelation of guilt by the mothers about withholding things from their daughters. The mothers responded with gestures of obedience to the doctor when he suggested further scrutiny of themselves rather than of their daughters in study of their problems.

Mrs. High's rationalization of her attention to Hilda's deviations as necessary to Hilda's welfare was shaken some more in this session by laughter from Karen and Alice. Alice brought out that the genesis of the illness lay in the parents' dependence on the child. The mothers' discussion of this brought out some vaguely hinted at guilt feelings.

Session 10

Mrs. High, Tenant, and Link spoke of their despair ("It is going on and on, seeing nothing ahead."), and how they missed their daughters. The daughters turned from them, with accusatory hints about being masculine. Laura asked, "Why did you take me to the bedroom?," and Hilda stated, "Hilda is man getting rough." The tension between mother and daughter was most clearly shown by Mrs. Link and Laura in a sort of despairing lovers' quarrel, with Laura again quite resentful of her mother's move to hospitalize her.

Mrs. Tenant expressed the mothers' feelings of being "just desperate." Hilda, in response to mother's request for her to "ask me a pertinent question," asked what mother would do for her cold when she came home. Mother answered that she would give her (only) nose drops. Hilda turned from mother.

Session 11

Hilda's negativism toward her mother was the main focus, with two patient visitors to the group, Alice and Vera, rather vocally encouraging Hilda to be "nice," and commenting on her prettiness. Hilda expressed antagonism toward the doctor's "clinics," stating, "I don't feel like going to Dr. Abrahams' clinics, let's go out," when her mother "gave in" to an attack on her as too demanding by Mrs. Knowland.

Alice explained to Mrs. Link that Laura's doubt as to whether she was her mother's daughter was similar to her own at the onset of her illness. Mrs. High told at length of her need for Hilda "to come out with something, have experience."

More thematic and situational continuity between the sessions has appeared. In the last two sessions more material emerged on the problem of the identity of the daughter as to sex and parentage. Hilda's response of somewhat disdainful protectiveness toward her mother when mother masochistically accepted attacks on herself was not a new development, but was more clearly expressed than formerly. Communication between the Links had moved to the point where there was open recrimination about Laura's status in the bedroom with mother, vis à vis Mr. Link. The mothers' feelings of despair and helplessness were also coming out.

The need of the mothers, as exemplified by Mrs. High, Mrs. Tenant and Mrs. Link, for a positive response the nature of which was not clear began to come out more sharply, as well as the self-punishing nature of their present relationships with their daughters.

The pattern of attack and defense changed gradually, as the mothers' defenses were breached by revelation, at times rivalrous, on the part of Mrs. Knowland, Mrs. Tenant, or Mrs. Link of the feelings the defensive mother (Mrs. High mostly) was unaware of. As noted before, this was first manifested in an action-identification (apparently on an ego level) with the dependent daughter of another mother. This revelation was exemplified in a succeeding session, when Mrs. Knowland, after one of Mrs. High's righteous attacks on Hilda, told of her anger when Karen was negativistic or too demanding. This moved Mrs. High to tell of her own anger and self-pity and also the consideration her daughter had for her.

With the gradual breaching of the mothers' defenses, the identification with the daughters took increasingly significant expression.

Session 12

Patients visiting the group (to "help the mothers") were quite vocal and direct in describing their own problems to the mothers. The low self-esteem of the daughter was brought out as related to derogation by the parents and also as stemming from missing mother. They went into the feeling of rejection and of hostility when making a choice between the parents, a choice the parents forced on them. When the visitors talked of their preference for father, Mrs. Tenant mentioned Tina's increasing adherence to her father.

The closing theme was that of crying without knowing why, with hints that it is related to needing mother. The mothers for the large part sat passively listening.

The underlying reason for this and subsequent visits by patients from the ward to the group were not clear, and await closer scrutiny of the records of the patients' group than is possible now. The patients visiting the group imparted vitally significant information to the parents. They seemed to be trying to relate themselves to what appeared as proxy parents, doing so in a somewhat patronizing "teaching" of the parents. Through this act they may have been getting back at their own. The interpersonal significance of their behavior was not determined because they never achieved any personal identity in this group, participating as self-appointed emissaries of the patients' therapy group, an action which the doctor acceded to in the experimental spirit. Their influence on the course of the mother-daughter group was small, inasmuch as the real problem in therapy, the revelation of the personal dependent identity of the members proceeded through an inevitable trial-and-error process. The patient visitors needed to be "digested" in this process to have any real effect on it, other than illuminating points here and there in the mother-daughter relationship.

5. APPEARANCE OF DAUGHTERS' FEELINGS ABOUT FOCAL ISSUES AND IDENTITY (*Sessions 16–31*)

The tangles the mother-daughter pair got into were participated in more clearly by the daughters, especially by Laura and Hilda and beginnings appeared of what were to become extremely meaningful cyclic sequences of behavior, with the theme of estrangement and reconciliation. The daughters, as the mothers had previously, joined together in expression of feelings, at first toward other mothers, and then their own. The mothers responded with verbalizing feelings about specific incidents in which daughter disappointed mother, though daughter acted as though she missed mother.

Session 16

Alice and Vera again visited the group.

The mothers at first spoke of the improvement of their daughters. Mrs. Knowland stated that Karen had learned from Alice not to talk to herself. Mrs. High told of Hilda's showing her consideration about her fatigue in coming to the hospital. That led to the question of giving a gift to the patient as to a child, and correcting her as a child. This was culminated in a statement that the daughter had mixed feelings about the gift, and was made childlike by it.

Hilda and Laura spilled their candy on the floor at this point. Mrs. High responded with vindictive helplessness, Mrs. Link with abject resignation, and Mrs. Tenant with enveloping ways toward Tina. Laura disconnectedly mentioned Thomas Jefferson and the Declaration of Independence, and said Tina was unable to express her feelings. When the doctor called for examination of the event, Mrs. Tenant expressed herself as darkly hopeless about understanding it, Mrs. High was somewhat more hopeful, and Mrs. Link wondered if her daughter understood her sensitivities. The visitors to the group then attempted to explain to the mothers their own and the daughters' feelings of wanting things and resenting needing them.

This sequence of behavior, in which the daughters acted out in a childish manner their strivings toward emancipation from mother, was the first in which the entire group participated in the issues involved. There was apparently no resolution of the issues in this session, but an initial joining of them. The mothers' feelings were expressed more clearly, and in relation to an actual happening in the group. The daughters expressed their feelings mainly through action and somewhat obscure verbalization (Laura's Thomas Jefferson and the Declaration of Independence) representing independence strivings. In addition Laura was undoubtedly pointing out her own problem in calling attention to Tina's inability to express her feelings. The visitors to the group served as a bridge between the mothers and daughters, this time less as educators, and closer to their identification with the daughters in feeling.

Session 17

Mrs. High and Mrs. Tenant early in the session showed despair over their daughters' conditions and responses. Mrs. Tenant told of her sleeplessness and her recent dreams of her daughter as an infant. The mothers returned to their despair, "abysmal feeling; defeated," when daughter deviated. Mrs. High stated, "We all feel that way," and whiningly brought out her resentment over Hilda's failure to answer while Mrs. High revealed her feelings in the group.

The mothers discussed how to make it up to their daughters, and their guilt and regret on not having taken care of them adequately. Mrs. High sadly mentioned Hilda's liking for her younger brother. Laura petulantly complained about being held in the hospital, after Alice voiced resentment toward her mother for having stopped her dating with boys.

This session seemed to be a continuation of the last one, with the mothers obliquely seeking reconciliation with the daughters. The increasing subjectivity of the patient-visitor was notable, marked by identification with the daughters. Mrs. Tenant's direct, unsophisticated dream material was in consonance with her functioning in other respects. It was dealt with as corroborative material by the doctor, and was not gone into further, since to do so would be a digression from the ego participation emphasis of this stage of therapy. Free association awaited greater capacity on the part of the group to associate freely.

Session 18

The chief focus at first was on the relationship of Mrs. Link and Laura, with Mrs. Link piteously crying about Laura's resentment and Laura in fragmentary manner acting tough, and then pleasant, as soon as mother cried. Both Laura and Hilda mentioned Susie, a patient who visited the group this session, and who spoke glowingly of her "lovely mother," as "an ugly kid, in actions, and underneath the skin." When Mrs. Link then told of Laura's misbehavior in the recent past, Laura spoke brutally of "killing cat's chicken" and her mother's use of her as a "colored girl." Mrs. Knowland told of her own disturbance as a little girl when her mother cut up chickens.

The group discussed ambition again, and the harmful effects of the lack of purposefulness of the environment of this section of the hospital. Mrs. Knowland exclaimed on the "good spirits" of this group.

Under the doctor's encouragement, the furious relationship between Mrs. Link and Laura again was revealed. With mother crying, Laura became friendlier to her, but kept her distance by pointing to Tina (apparently, as in the past, meaning herself) as a "crazy girl," and the doctor as a woman.

Through the focus on the Links, the session went through a cycle of mother dependently pleading with daughter for response, daughter responding with hostility, mother despairingly withdrawing, daughter temporarily triumphant, but despising herself. As usual, other members entered, Hilda through an attack on a patient who glorified her mother, and Mrs. Knowland apparently identifying as a little girl in regard to mother's brutality. More data appeared on the cycle of distance between mother and daughter, anguish by mother, and friendly but guilty overture by daughter. Mother apparently could not express her hostility or relinquish daughter, stopping her expression of feeling at despair.

Session 19

Mrs. Knowland, reflecting the mothers' fear of the anger of the patients, brought out her preoccupation with the strong "smouldering" feelings shown in the group and her fear that Karen would reject her. Mrs. Link stated that though she hated to see Laura get upset, the experience of the last meeting had helped.

Karen's and Hilda's baiting of their mothers as a sort of power operation, a turning of the tables, was broached by Mrs. Knowland. Hilda in this vein stated that she liked "Dr. Abrahams' troubles." Mrs. Knowland revealed her guilt feelings on putting Karen in the hospital to "put her out of the way."

The mothers discussed why they were so "different to that one person," this daughter, and why this daughter showed indifference to them, talked about them to others, but talked of others while with mother. Mrs. Link illustrated by relating that Laura asked the nurses about her. Mrs. Tenant's statement that she did not have that trouble with Tina was received with great soundless laughter by Karen. Mrs. Knowland pointed to Tina's lack of anger as related to her mother's way of not rousing antagonism.

Mrs. High talked of Hilda's acts of resistance toward being put in school and subsequent preference of others to her mother. Alice stated, "Maybe you pet her too much!"

Mrs. Knowland reported that Karen was talking more clearly at home. Alice and Laura spoke of the "father in the cellar" as being on Laura's mind, and laughed when Laura stated that if she had a husband, she would lock him in the cellar.

Mrs. High reported that Hilda told her definitely that she didn't want to go out because her mother wanted her to.

This session reflected the growing awareness of the mothers of both their own anxieties, and their daughters' feelings. There seemed to be a more objective inquiry into the relationship of mother and daughter. New lines of inquiry seemed to be present into the uniqueness of the relationship with this particular child. The daughter was perversely resistant to mother when with her. She was preoccupied with her when away. This was broached as usual on the basis of the behavior of the daughter. There was also freer and more understandable use of symbolic action language, such as "father in the cellar," relating probably to sexual rivalry with mothers, also submission to her possessiveness, as did father.

Session 20

Conformity or deviation of the daughters in making the perfectionist mothers happy or unhappy, hopeful or resigned, was discussed with warmth by Mrs. High and Mrs. Knowland. Mrs. High held that she couldn't be happy unless Hilda was making sense, by showing continuity of thought. Mrs. High complained that her husband told her, on this, that she wanted the world with a ribbon tied around it. When Mrs. Knowland claimed that he might be just trying to push the whole thing away, Mrs. High stated that he cried at the idea that Hilda wasn't well along with his other daughters. Mrs. High then brought out how her husband was like Mrs. Knowland's, in his criticism of her.

Session 21

Mrs. Knowland brought out, "I'm callous; instead of mourning, I'm beaming," in denying the dependency expressed by Mrs. Link and the other mothers on a satisfactory response from the daughters. The discussion of satisfaction with this child led to discussion of whether mother wanted a boy or a girl. Except for Mrs. High, who asserted that she was joyful over Hilda's birth, the mothers claimed they had wanted a boy. Hilda told of having "bad" feelings on being hospitalized.

In the last two sessions, the discussion of the mothers' dependence on the daughters took the group into discussion of criticism by the husband, similarities with him, and rejection of this girl child because it was not a boy. Mrs. High approached consideration of her husband as a disapproving masculine figure through talking of Mrs. Knowland's.

The rejection of the daughter as a girl, coupled with feelings of mourning, as expressed by Mrs. Knowland, was followed in the next few sessions by expression of an intransigent wish on daughter's part for mother to be daughter's emotional age, and on the mother's part for daughter to act as an adult. Mrs. High brought in as a preoccupation of hers, the image of her husband as not accepting her ambitions.

Session 27

The group was at first withdrawn. After preliminaries, in which Mrs. Knowland encouraged her, Mrs. High apologetically criticized Hilda's scratching her face, and Hilda retaliated with a prolonged reprimand to her mother for a previous hospitalization, then told of her desire to leave the ward and be a woman surgeon. She told, in opposition to her mother, who stated she had no confidence in her, that she had once been proud, but had been away from home a long time. Karen snickered at this.

Mrs. High and Mrs. Knowland then commented on their daughters' destructiveness and masturbation, respectively. Mrs. High described her own helplessness and Hilda's maliciousness. Mrs. Tenant and Mrs. Link told of their desperation, their daughters' priority over their own needs. "Life is a burden" without their daughters. Hilda stated that she was destructive "because Dr. Hall gives me vitamin pills." Mrs. Link spoke up for Hilda, saying that she was unable to help herself. Laura was derogatory to Mrs. High, referring to fecal material. Mrs. Tenant hopelessly felt "like Tina is a two- to three-year-old," but she stated that Laura enjoyed herself better. Mrs. High was hopeless about Hilda's habit of "building a romance about a person."

Mrs. High's hostile attentiveness to Hilda's hostile ways resulted in Hilda's reprimand to mother and identification with a surgeon. The Knowlands entered the fray in a manner hostile to Hilda who had blamed separation from mother for her actions. Then all the mothers blamed the daughters for their own dependent, lost feelings. Hilda talked on the issue of being cared for—in this case, by others.

The Links identified with Hilda, and spoke up for Hilda as helpless and Laura attacked Mrs. High in anal terms. This brought out Mrs. High's ambivalence toward her daughter, turning to Laura for the positive aspect. Mrs. High reflected this note in talking about Hilda's romantic relationship to others.

This session was a further instance of the mulling over the group was doing around the issue of responsibility for their hostile, disjunctive, despairing feelings. The relationship of the Highs was apparently still cast up in the group process as best representing the situation of the mothers and daughters, or at any rate, the one they revealed in interaction with this particular doctor.

To review it again, it was marked by dependent attack by a mother, retaliation by her daughter, entrance of another mother-daughter pair, then all the mothers against the daughters with assertion of their own helplessness. Then another mother-daughter pair moved closer to direct feelings. Mrs. Tenant brought hers out most directly, as a split ambivalence between Tina and someone else. Mrs. High picked this last note up, referring indirectly to the cause of much of her hopelessness, Hilda's leaving her for another. The group took a roundabout way of getting there, but all participated in the problem at hand, a mutual recrimination between mother and daughter over the issue of abandonment.

Session 28

Mrs. High told of a recent episode where Hilda helped her. Mrs. Link brought up Laura's smearing of herself with lipstick for her brothers. When Mrs. Knowland attacked Mrs. High for pushing Hilda "to help her," Mrs. High claimed she had gained the point with Hilda, that Hilda had committed the crime first.

Mrs. High called her daughter too demanding. Mrs. Tenant decried Tina's timidity. Mrs. Link came out with Laura's fear of being killed.

Tina and Hilda attempted to turn from their mothers, in their characteristic ways. Mrs. Link and Mrs. High took opposite sides about Hilda's willfulness. Mrs. High then followed Mrs. Link's hopefulness about Laura with grudging admission of Hilda's improvement, "though she is still imperfect."

The doctor asked for examination of the meaning of mother's high standards, and Mrs. Link vaguely brought out her concern with conscience, and Mrs. Tenant spoke of Tina as being too quiet. Mrs. Link stated that Hilda seemed to think she was in the hospital for the rest of her life.

Hilda then asked if she would be in the hospital for all of her life, and the doctor encouraged expression of her thoughts and feelings on this. Hilda expressed her wayward thoughts, of thinking of other people.

The attentiveness of the mothers to their daughters continued along the lines of past sessions. Mrs. High was concerned with Hilda's initiative in helping mother this time. Mrs. Link was attentive to Laura's acting up and paying attention to her brother. Mrs. Knowland's concern with Mrs. High's problems resulted in discussion of who had started the destructive process mother and daughter were engaged in.

Mrs. High, Mrs. Tenant, and Mrs. Link then turned to attributes of the daughters, along the lines of their own preoccupations, whereupon the daughters turned as usual from the mothers. This was discussed briefly by Mrs. High and Mrs. Link, with Mrs. Link taking Mrs. Knowland's place in defending Hilda. She later told of her conscience and related it indirectly to the indefinite hospitalization of Hilda, an indirect approach on her own initiative to her problem with her daughter. Through participation in the Highs' problems she made progress in facing her own.

Session 29

Mrs. High was despondent over Hilda's and her own unchanged ways, and Hilda appeared angry and openly defiant. This Mrs. High took to be retrogression, and speaking of losing control of herself, cried. Mrs. Tenant and Mrs. High joined in expressions of despondency. Laura seemed to support Hilda by a statement about Hilda keeping herself clean.

Mrs. High came out with her desire to shake the stubbornness and unresponsiveness out of Hilda, although Hilda in a saintly manner responded in assent to the doctor's question about her desire to get well. When Mrs. Tenant stated, "I almost die when Tina cries," Mrs. Link related an exuberant tale of Laura's improvement.

Hilda and Karen showed antagonism in marked form (mocking noises, leaving the room, masturbating) as Mrs. High talked about Hilda's stubbornness again and threatened violence to the characters who fill Hilda's obsessive thoughts. Hilda expressed doubt, in an exchange with the doctor, concerning expression of her feelings, as contrasted with expressing her escape thoughts.

This was followed in the next sessions (30 and 31) with clearly expressed independence manifestations ("live my life") by the patients, and mention of fear of the daughters' deaths by the mothers. The mothers expressed intense feelings of hopelessness "almost die when Tina cries") and that the daughters were lost to them but needed the mothers to lead their lives for them. This was gradually followed by expression of violent intent toward the fantasy figures the daughters turned to and then toward the daughters themselves. The mothers expressed a sense of martyrdom, with a growing awareness of having unacceptable feelings toward their daughters. They began directly asking their daughters what they had against them, with fragmentary replies at first that the daughters did not like them.

The movement of these sessions was toward facing the issue of and the feelings involved in the separation of mother and daughter, and realization of their own identities. Coincidentally, the expression of hostility by the mothers and communication among them about themselves as individuals appeared.

6. Appearance of Acceptance by Mothers of Their Own Problems as Individuals (Sessions 32–51)

The movement in communication between mothers and daughters evidenced in previous phases gained strength and clarity, with violent interchanges about receiving love from one another. The mothers brought in for discussion problems in living other than the one with the daughter. Similarities between mother and daughter in their developmental history were brought out.

Session 32

The mothers seemed to ignore Hilda's flat, intransigent statement about another patient who was home now, and went on to their shame over expressing their anger. Mrs. High and Mrs. Knowland differed on whether they had changed since their youth, and on how deeply they were hurt. Mrs. High stated that she was just as when she was young. She told of her impulse to shake Hilda when she misbehaved, and Mrs. Link related a recent incident where her daughter showed anger toward her. Mrs. Knowland told of accepting Karen's critical statements. Mrs. High expressed irritation at Hilda's maneuvers to keep distant.

The mothers then talked about being ashamed of this child. Mrs. Link cited such shame as weakness, Mrs. Tenant disclaimed it, and hinted that Tina meant more to her than her other children. She led most of the mothers to agree that they were martyrs. When Mrs. Knowland disagreed she was told she was kidding herself. Mrs. High brought up her own tantrums at home nowadays, and that she was fed up (with the martyrdom). She interjected that the possible death of her husband would make things worse.

Hilda asked a question about a Miss Fight, and the lively discussion of the mothers froze. The doctor investigated the reason for this and the mothers returned to a discussion of their guilt when they were away from their daughters. Mrs. Tenant claimed others were saying she was an unfeeling woman, and that that was the cause of her daughter's illness. In the next breath, Mrs. Tenant criticized Mrs. High for hanging onto the doctor's last word.

Hilda's provocative statement set the mothers off onto their problem of handling their hostility. Their preoccupation with this child and their shame over this preoccupation as weakness was revealed. Their strong sense of separateness or martyrdom as incident to their relationship with this child was discussed. Mrs. High's reference to the possibility of the (wished) death of her husband as helping in the family situation (brought out as the converse) brought forth a comment from Hilda on a Miss Fight (one of her many fantasy figures).

Anxiety became open then, and the mothers expressed their guilt when away from their daughters. Mrs. Tenant's defense against the accusation that her lack of feelings caused her daughter's illness brought her underlying problem into clearer focus. Mrs. Tenant then turned on Mrs. High, paving the way for further communication between them on each other's characters and motives.

Session 36

Mrs. High keynoted the meeting by bringing out her new search for meaning in Hilda's behavior, and in her own feelings. She told of her perfectionistically self-defeating inability to please herself in her art work. A controversy between Mrs. Knowland, who had "been brought up to worry" and had taken on other, more stoical ways, and Mrs. Tenant who led the others in asserting their helpless preoccupation with their daughters, led to tears on Mrs. High's part. Mrs. Roper and Mrs. High agreed on their "brave front and otherwise insides," and Rae cried.

Then came an abrupt swing toward "cracking" the daughters for misdeeds by Mrs. High; and Hilda attacked Rae, who was crying, by pulling her hair.

Hilda spoke to the doctor of her dislike for her mother as the cause of her destructiveness, and apologized to mother for it when Mrs. High directly asked Hilda why she didn't like her. Mrs. Roper brought out the closeness between herself and Rae, Rae's sense of inferiority and domination of her mother before her illness. Comparisons were drawn among Rae and Hilda and Karen by their mothers.

Hilda expressed her dislike of the hospital and her maltreatment. She expressed to the doctor her preference for a woman doctor and Mrs. High likewise expressed her "hollow acceptance" of that, and her underlying feeling of tearing her hair out over that statement.

This session was marked by extension of Mrs. High's awareness of her perfectionistically self-defeating tactics with Hilda and in other areas of her life, and receptivity for the meaning her daughter attempted to convey to her. There was more open expression (verbal and action) by Hilda of her desperate hostility toward her present mode of life and the people around her who are associated with that life, including her mother.

The mothers agreed on the "false, brave fronts" they put up, and their helpless preoccupations with their daughters. In her attack on weeping Rae, Hilda may have been duplicating her mother's "false, brave front."

This session combined elements of the previous ones, but with more consciously motivated investigation on the part of the mothers into their problems as individuals and their relationships to their daughters.

The closeness of the mother and daughter prior to the illness and at present, and the mother's jealous feelings in regard to daughter's interest in others entered into the discussions, in clearer, but still fragmentary form. The pained and oppositional feelings of the daughter in reference to mother and of mother to her husband came out.

Session 38

Mrs. Knowland mentioned herself as being an "opposition spirit" in reference to her husband. Rae spoke to her mother on "tired"(ness) as the reason she turned away from her. Mrs. Knowland, on the other hand, stated that Rae opposed her mother's demand for "wisdom and prudency."

Mrs. Link and Mrs. Roper gave instances of their daughters' overriding natures, of being called by the name the husband calls them, and verbally treating them (the mothers) like children, while themselves objecting to being treated that way. Why they deserved such treatment was discussed consensually by Mrs. Tenant, Link, and Roper, with Mrs. Tenant voicing it as "some terrible thing it must have been," and their hopelessness about their own happiness. Rae kissed her mother on the mouth on leaving.

The possessiveness of mother and daughter in the family constellation as following from the anxiety of mother in relation to husband seemed to be discussed here. The picture as presented by the mothers appeared to be one of the mother who, when "opposite" to the husband on issues of control and dominance, turned to daughter possessively and dependently. Daughter reciprocated this possessiveness, taking a supervisory relationship, but also ambivalently reacted to mother as mother did to her husband.

Session 39

Mrs. Knowland, through mention of a magazine article on criminals, noted that the patients had unsuspected abilities. She pressed Hilda (whose mother was absent) and Laura for comment. They both disclaimed interest, although Hilda was dressed and wearing makeup. On the doctor's questioning, Laura stated an interest in sewing, but then turned angrily on him. This led to a discussion of the alternation of the daughters' desire for affection and resentment which Mrs. Link brought out with incidents.

Hilda came out with a philosophical statement about life being wrong and said she had a pain, pointing to her left chest. She suddenly asked for her brother.

Mrs. Tenant asked about Tina's relation with the others on the ward, in a manner new to her, and took the blame for Tina's dependence on people. When the doctor pointed out Tina's bossy ways, Laura bossily turned on her mother and the doctor.

Hilda forcefully brought out that she preferred a patient to everyone in the room but her mother, and then asked about the "freshness" of several overtly homosexual patients. Laura became aggressively playful toward the doctor. Hilda asked what hell was like. At the end of the hour, Mrs. Knowland submissively asked her reluctant daughter what they should do the next day.

A notable aspect of this session was the progression of the group to discussion of the feelings of the daughters. Hilda displayed her sadness apparently relative to her deeply dependent relationship to mother, indirectly relating it to the hell of a homosexual love relationship. Then Mrs. Tenant's new-found curiosity about how Tina actually got along on the ward brought on references by the patients to the nature of their life on the ward. The group was coming closer to clearer discussion of its issues, without early resort to anticipatory despair or rejection of one another.

Session 40

Hilda asked for an operation, by a woman surgeon. The theme of lack of faith in self and unsureness of self was brought out by Mrs. Knowland and Mrs. Roper. They stated that their own unsureness made them bad for their daughters, but then attacked their husbands for being nervous.

Mrs. High and Mrs. Knowland noted the bossiness of their daughters. Hilda then challenged her mother to find out why she had torn her clothes. Destructiveness by the daughter as having emotional meaning was accepted by all the mothers, including Mrs. Tenant, whose daughter had torn her dress down the back. Karen threatened to give her mother a brown felt hat.

Speaking up then became the issue; Mrs. Tenant appealed to Tina through the group to do so. Hilda instead spoke up, asking for Mrs. Link, and her question was called a habit by Mrs. High (referring to Hilda's talking about other people when with her).

Hilda shouted, "Truman, he's my obsession." Karen and Laura noted theirs, Karen's involving "back and envelopes," and Laura's "Roosevelt." Tina's was stated by Laura as "no nose." Mrs. High became tense, denying emotional significance to these expressions.

Mrs. Knowland encouraged Karen to tell why she chewed her dress and was answered, "It tastes altogether too good." Mrs. High stated that they didn't speak the same language. Hilda answered with an obscure statement about her eye hurting. After Mrs. Knowland bragged of Karen's co-operativeness at home, Mrs. High noted Hilda's mention of a patient who had gone home and her envy of this patient's emotional expressiveness.

In this session there was more open meaningful display by the daughters of their preoccupations and of their wish for more open emotional expressiveness. This followed the evidence of curiosity on the part of the mothers about how their daughters lived. Mrs. Knowland mentioned the mothers' lack of faith in themselves and unsureness of selves as bad for their daughters, and their husbands' nervousness in turn as bad for them.

The meeting was remarkable for the relative orderliness and purposefulness of the interchange, and the amount of consensual data that were voiced between mother and daughter. Mrs. Knowland continued to lead the mothers in expression of their failings in regard to their daughters and their husbands' failings toward them.

The daughters' preoccupation in reference to change of sex came up again, somewhat clearer than in the past. The semantic veiling of meaning (Truman, Roosevelt, back and envelopes, etc.) by the daughters indicated considerable emotional distance between mother and daughter, but was still an approach to specific communication.

Their desperate hopelessness of receiving from one another what they felt was love, coupled with a show of obdurate violence by daughter to her own or another mother, and their pleading for encouragement and help became more evident in the next few sessions.

Session 41

Before the meeting, Hilda struck out at her mother who had tried to have her return a banana she had taken from Tina. Hilda then reluctantly complied. Mrs. High complained of Hilda's perfectionism in reference to her art work. Mrs. Link brought up Laura's resentment and the mothers agreed that the daughters resented them, but didn't know why.

Mrs. High brought in Hilda's talking of other things and the mothers agreed that all the daughters did that. Hilda mentioned being helped and Laura stated she didn't like the whole bunch and resented people staring at her. Hilda mentioned the week end, "which means doom" to her, asked for the dance therapist and said, "about Sunday night, I don't, I do." Mrs. High agreed with Hilda's statement about not liking life, "since she became ill at an early age."

The mothers agreed on the lifelong opposition of the daughters to them, and Hilda tore a magazine. Laura and Rae laughed when Mrs. High said despairingly, "There's nothing to work on in Hilda." There was an exchange between Hilda and Laura, with Laura derogatory about getting well, and Hilda compliantly stated, "I'm getting well." Mrs. High agreed with the doctor's interpretation that she was depending on Hilda to get well on her own initiative.

Rae cowered on her mother's mention of shock treatment as a means of getting well. The other daughters showed fear and anger. Mrs. Knowland brought out that Karen was not resentful of her now, and that she differed from the other mothers in desiring to change herself, not Karen. Hilda stated she was "thinking about daddy long legs" . . . and "don't like Saint Elizabeths." The fear of violence when the daughter took the initiative came up again.

Hilda's blow at her mother keynoted a particularly stormy session. The daughters' lifelong opposition to the mothers and the emptiness of their current lives came out in a clearer form. Mrs. Knowland again somewhat smugly expressed her difference from the others in her desire to change herself. The mothers' fear of the daughters' violence was expressed. The daughters took more of the initiative in the meeting than formerly. There was also a greater understanding expressed by the mothers for the daughters, in regard to their current problems in living in the hospital.

Session 42

The meeting was marked by an open clash between Mrs. High and Mrs. Knowland on correcting Hilda. A great deal of material on masculinity-femininity came up, relative to fruit, red hair, bumping the other person and the sex of Hilda's brother as now male, rather than the previous female.

Hilda, as in previous sessions, seemed to be reconsidering more overtly her concept of self from an independent, unfeeling, potentially violent masculine character, to a lonely creature needing affection and help, who associated receiving food with receiving love. Mrs. High was openly ambivalent toward Hilda.

Session 43

The chief area of interaction was between Mrs. High and Hilda, who early in the session tore her dress. Hilda's destructive way of showing her feelings of independence, and sensitivity to others' criticism were recognized by Mrs. High as similar to her own sensitivity as a child, which led her to truancy and escapism.

Mrs. Knowland took up for Hilda as a rebel and noted the feeling of power Hilda must have derived from her systematic tearing of her dress. Mrs. High finally saw Hilda's act as one of resentment "at the sting of it all," but objected to its unconventionality.

Mrs. High's and Mrs. Knowland's concern with conventionality were brought out as opposites. Mrs. High told of her childhood unconventionality and Mrs. Knowland of actively fostering unconventionality in her child in resentment of her own conventional childhood.

Mrs. Roper stated that her experience with Rae was similar to Mrs. High's with Hilda. Rae's contrary statements of satisfaction with the hospital and yet submissive asking mother to hold her hand when the problem of independence was talked about, were discussed.

Session 44

Rae was antagonistic toward her mother, but expressed friendly feelings toward her father, Mrs. Knowland, and the doctor before the meeting. Mrs. High was antagonistic toward Hilda for her childishness, and Mrs. Knowland defended Hilda. Mrs. High attacked the doctor as not answering anything after he pointed out her insistence on only her own answers from Hilda. Mrs. High and Mrs. Roper commented on the cut-off point where their daughters stopped them from further communication.

Hilda then revealed negativism, "I don't like the meeting . . . . for the purpose of . . . . it feels more comfortable that way." This opened up a discussion of Hilda's mode of exposing her genitalia by her sitting posture, and Hilda commented in reply on "the twenty cats someone has" (a woman doctor on the staff had many cats in her quarters) and named a number of friends she had had in camp.

Mrs. High revealed that her talking about things Hilda was interested in was "just to get her going my way." This activity was a great strain on Mrs. High, for which strain she stated she had been helped by the doctor. She objected to Hilda's ways as not normal, and that an openly antagonistic assertion of independence by Hilda would demonstrate that she was normal: "Hilda acts that way to get my goat, reach my feelings."

In these sessions, the area of understanding and tolerance between mothers and daughters was widened by the recognition of the daughter as a sensitive, unconventional person, quite like the mother in her childhood. Unconventionality and antagonism as present in a daughter because it "feels more comfortable that way" (Hilda), and the mothers' interest in the child as "just to get her going my way," were brought out as preludes to a gradual but intense hostile interchange of recrimination and guilt both over abandonment of the child to the hospital, and over letting go of the image of the daughter as an infant. The transformation of the situation

of the overriding infantile demand into that of compliance
to the wishes of the other was illustrated by Hilda and her
mother in their comments on exposure of genitals and talking
about what the other was interested in. Hilda exposed herself because a woman doctor wanted her to, as evidenced by
this doctor's keeping a "cat house." Mrs. High complied with
her daughter's interests to realize her own ends. In this process the mothers revealed more of their feelings of helplessness
about realizing their own wishes and empathy with the daughters' suffering.

The group showed more independence from the doctor.
Self-direction by the group toward its goals of changing itself
appeared. Both mothers and daughters showed initiative, although chiefly through pointing out the other's lack of it. As
Mrs. Tenant coddled Tina, who constantly looked at herself
in a mirror, Mrs. High said in the forty-seventh session, "If
she were my child, I would let go of her hand and take the
mirror away and see what would happen. What have you
got to lose?"

Session 46

After she had introduced the concept of unconscious through
a question, Mrs. Knowland noted that Mrs. High's idea of dealing with her own lack of awareness was through concentrating
on Hilda's lack. Mrs. High nevertheless followed her usual mode
of attacking Hilda for her lack of will to go home, and angrily
stated there was plenty of love and affection for her there.

Hilda mentioned her brother's name when the doctor pos-
ited a visit home for her, and her mother became angry and despairing, and threatened to visit Hilda less frequently. There followed an interchange where Hilda intimated that she knew the
thought underlying her mother's usual rejective move.

Rae stated she never would get over her home. This led to a
controversy over whether the daughters were aware of things,
with the development of a discussion between Mrs. High and

Hilda over Hilda's feeling her nails were ruined by her mother's order. (Hilda defiantly scratched her own face frequently; in this case mother's attitude was tantamount to an order.)

Mrs. Knowland and Mrs. High compared their reactions to loss of another person's approval. Mrs. High claimed acceptance of that loss as a challenge, except when she lost her husband's approval. Mrs. Knowland attempted to get a reply to her despairing plea to Karen not to masturbate. Mrs. High agreed with the doctor that she shook off the meeting at its end, as if it hadn't happened, and she accepted the doctor's delineation of this escape mechanism.

The controversy over affection and home, whether mother has affection for daughter and what home meant to daughter, moved into areas hitherto untouched—what underlay mother's rejective act. Mrs. High's emotional susceptibility to the loss of her husband's approval (perhaps getting rid of daughter for husband) was broached. Mrs. Knowland at this point for the first time verbally brought up Karen's masturbation.

Session 47

Mrs. Springer, her sister Miss Sheppard, and Sally Springer were present for the first time. The other mothers summed up a great deal of what they had learned about their attitudes toward their daughters by way of orienting them to the group procedure. Mrs. Knowland told of the compulsive way the mothers required the daughters to live up to their standards in the group, and their way of complaining about their daughters.

Mrs. High noted the importance of treating the daughter appropriately to the situation, not making the daughter comfortable by babying her. Mrs. Roper commented on the futility of advice per se, and the need to understand the situation. Hilda was openly ambivalent, showing interest in her mother's "cultural" topics, and also her latest reiterative one about nails and cuticles, which annoyed her mother.

Miss Sheppard asked the doctor about the effect of chiding the daughter (her sister's behavior toward Sally). The doctor called her attention to the Highs' experience with this problem. Mrs. Springer's assertions about body building for mental health were attacked by the mothers and Hilda, and laughed at by her daughter. The old members of the group seemed encouraged by describing what they had learned.

Session 48

Hilda was pertinent, peremptory and self-assured about her wishes for the doctor to close the door and her mother not to baby her in regard to wearing a coat. Mrs. High defensively claimed her attacks were necessary because of Hilda's antagonism. Mrs. Knowland defended Hilda as aloof but intelligible, and protected Sally from Miss Sheppard's domination.

The focus then went to Mrs. Tenant and Mrs. Tenant's baby-ing of Tina all her life, for "her security. . . . she lives in fear." Mrs. Tenant was attacked by Mrs. High: "If she were my child, I would let go of her hand and take the mirror away and see what would happen. What have you got to lose?" Both Mrs. Tenant and Mrs. High became angry at each other, but deflected it by referring to their daughters' happiness or anger as the deter-minants of their own behavior.

Mrs. High's alternative defense of indifference was attacked by Mrs. Knowland as "detached motherliness." She then claimed that Mrs. High showed affection for Mrs. Tenant in her criticism.

Mrs. High compared Hilda's misbehavior to a killer's reasons for killing. Hilda indicated her feelings by recounting a "think-ing of" sequence of flight and fight, but reluctantly agreed to see her mother when she came next time.

In this session both Hilda and Mrs. High were peremp-tory, Hilda to the doctor and her mother, and Mrs. High to Mrs. Tenant about relinquishment of her defenses of baby-ing Tina through allowing Tina to develop. Then a mutual show of anger brought them dependently to attack their daughters as responsible for their unhappiness. Mrs. High and Hilda went through a display of their hostile feelings to a reluctant but voluntary reconciliation. This made the completion of a full cycle of behavior on the part of Mrs. High and Hilda, where they displayed in recognizable form, over a series of sessions, estranged dependency, deviation of daughter from mother's defense, despair and anger on mother's part, threat of and abandonment of each other, with recrimination over the past and present, remorse, and reconciliation. Both were now somewhat less dependent on one another in the group.

Session 49

Mrs. High in a reflective mood recounted Hilda's powers of observation of others and attempts to get well. She went on, stating that she told Hilda of her own feeling that she has to change her moods, ways, and that it is a long drawn-out process. Her reaction to Hilda's "other people" was one of anxiety and some curiosity now, and she attempted to foster independent action in Hilda.

She revealed that she would consider Hilda well when she showed talent and enjoyed it. Sadly, she related that now she would settle for just social acceptability. Hilda stated: "Giving in."

Hilda stated, "I don't like life." Mrs. High reacted with her usual rejection. Mrs. Knowland reproved Mrs. High as unfeeling, and as failing to provide something in the relationship. Mrs. High stated that Hilda felt that way because she had had all unpleasant experiences so far. She, too, had moments of not liking life, but she dealt differently with this feeling.

At this point, Hilda showed, though she was antagonistic to her mother when her mother rejected her way of talking, initiative in attempting to please her mother during the course of the meeting, by attempting to turn on lights. Laura acidly commented, "Look at the dirty cat," as Mrs. High showed sadness over Hilda's ways. Hilda stated, "Piece of wood," when asked by her mother about her fears.

The mother-daughter relationship was particularly overt today, with Hilda making overt attempts to please Mrs. High, and Mrs. High recounting her new-found curiosity about Hilda's feelings and obsessional characters. Hilda brought out a connection between recovery and the mother-daughter relationship, i.e., it would mean submitting to another. The process of differentiation continued, as Mrs. High brought out her empathy with Hilda, but also brought out wherein she differed from her.

Mrs. Knowland continued to identify with Hilda and criticize Mrs. High for her shortcomings as a mother.

Session 51

Karen started by saying apropos of whether to see the *Snake Pit*, "giving them a good, tough time—the effect was horrid." Mrs. Springer spoke of the things Sally was denied, and how she couldn't enjoy herself without Sally. Sally laughed, and appealed seductively to the doctor, stating, "What else is there to do?"

Miss Sheppard saw meaning in Sally's usually obscure talk, and Sally stated, "Are we living because they are dead, or are we dead because they are living?" Hilda joined in, mocking Mrs. Springer, who claimed what Sally needed was a man's sexual love. Mrs. Springer recommended the doctor for this purpose and attacked her sister, Miss Sheppard, as possessive of her child.

Sally expressed feelings of being dead because of lack of affection and also her murderous feelings. These were replied to by Mrs. Springer, with the seemingly incongruous statement that Sally needed aggressive leadership by a girl, as active as Mrs. Springer. She told of arranging it with Vera (who happened to be an aggressive homosexual patient).

The patients laughed and Karen voiced reluctance to "starting business." Sally spoke sarcastically and bitterly of her mother. Hilda methodically tore her dress. Mrs. Springer stated she had done poorly by Sally, and again asserted she wanted to share the things that were important to her (outdoor body building fads) with Sally.

The relationship of Sally and her mother was discussed by the group through most of this session. In a manner reminiscent of the earlier behavioral sequences of the Highs, Mrs. Springer spoke with anxiety of how she missed Sally. Sally in a futile manner abandoned Mrs. Springer to the doctor, and was defended by her aunt. Hilda mocked her, much as Karen had mocked Mrs. High earlier. Mrs. Springer attacked Sally through recommendations (which carried rejection of the daughter's feelings) of what she needed, in this case based on her own defenses of the past and present, "a man's love" and vigorous feminine leadership, naming a markedly homosexual patient.

Sally expressed herself bitterly and Hilda tore her dress. Mrs. Springer asked for reconciliation with Sally, but on her own terms.

7. Appearance of Group-Centered Discussions and Full Cyclic Sequences of the Mother-Daughter Pairs (Sessions 52–96)

By the fifty-second session, the group had turned the corner on achieving an identity of its own. Resistances toward the doctor became less obstructive and the group became able to center its attention on its own initiative on its problems. Mothers and daughters began to complete their sequences of estrangement and hostile retaliation with open reconciliation.

The daughters and mothers spoke on the same subject, a concrete sign of rapprochement. The mothers talked more freely about their weaknesses, indicating a diminished need to be superior. The mothers began to think of themselves as like their daughters, rather than as utterly different. The communication of the daughters became progressively less obscure, and met with an increasingly appropriate feeling response from the mothers.

There was evident change in the relationship between the group and the doctor. Feelings toward him were more openly expressed, as when Mrs. High told him in the sixty-fifth meeting that she was disappointed in him as well as in her daughter; genuine appeals were made for his help and the mothers accepted his guidance. The problem which he had originally posed—i.e., of what was going on between the mothers and daughters—had now been accepted by the mothers, to the point of recognizing the feelings they had toward one another; following the doctor's guidance, they could begin to examine the source of these feelings. This was possible also because their defenses had been breached to some extent. Their work became more consistent in individual meetings, and carried over from one meeting to the next, so that the sixty-fifth meeting was opened with reference to the unfinished business of the week before. The meaning of what went on in meetings became more manifest in the verbal content, because of the increase in directness and diminution in ambivalence. Meetings from here on can be summarized with less risk of significant distortion.

Session 52

Hilda talked at first of her lonely week ends making her upset, and Mrs. High got around, after her usual attack on Hilda for running away the other day, to remembering that Hilda had stated she was disturbed when she was running away. Miss Sheppard, Mrs. Knowland, and Mrs. Springer interpreted the act as a try at freedom, and that Hilda was "following a different path." Mrs. High then showed sympathy and sensitivity to Hilda's expression of impatience and inability to take further discussion. Communication of feelings was talked about next; Mrs. Knowland came out with Karen's expectation of being called childish and Mrs. Tenant with Tina's timidity and fears of doing something wrong. Mrs. Knowland formulated it as a failure of the mothers to help them develop their own way of doing things, "so they do things in order to annoy us or to please us and expect us to set the standard."

Mrs. Springer and then Hilda attacked the life in the hospital as contributing to apprehensiveness. This led to expression by the mothers of apprehension about the public's pity and hostility. Mrs. Springer and Mrs. Knowland spoke of hiding feelings by avoidance or by laughter. Mrs. Tenant was bitter about "the stigma."

This was apparently the signal for a complete job of tearing her dress by Hilda. Sally stated, "I think it is inside." Hilda followed with, "hole in the ground."

Mrs. High accepted the tearing of the dress as communication of feeling by Hilda, and Hilda mentioned two sets of women's names, those people who hindered and those who helped her. Mrs. Springer blamed herself for transmitting fear to her daughter, as did Mrs. Knowland. On the doctor's suggestion, Hilda agreed to discuss the problem further in the group.

This session is an excellent demonstration of the developing therapeutic dynamism, of the way the mother-daughter sequence is participated in by the entire group. After Hilda mentioned her feelings of aloneness on week ends, Mrs. High came around, after an initial attack, to accepting Hilda's recent elopement as emotionally determined. Various mothers then projected their (latent) motivation onto the act, and Mrs. High with their support seemed to empathize more deeply with her daughter. Then several mothers (Mrs. Springer, Mrs. Tenant, and Mrs. Knowland) did the same with their daughters, and a general formulation was advanced on a cause of the difficulties with the daughters—failure to help the daughter achieve independent development (a step toward realization of their own failure on this score and their dependent status). Apprehension about a number of things, especially other people's opinions, was voiced by a number of people, with a rising tide of bitterness, culminating in destruction of her dress by Hilda, the most demonstrative person in the group. Then this act was associated to by a number of people with emphasis on its emotional determinants.

The group dynamism is fairly well advanced with ability to carry through the session on focal issues and themes, and to talk about these in relation to persons and events in the group.

Session 53

Mrs. Springer complained that Sally was "overstimulated" during a football game that afternoon, and had stood on her head, exposing herself, and later kicked and booted people. Mrs. Springer and Miss Sheppard at first denied Sally's ability to remember it. Mrs. High attacked Sally as irrelevant, as Sally and Hilda came out with their obscure verbalizations and mocking behavior. As the doctor focused on Mrs. High's attitude, she sympathized with Hilda when she was looked down on. Sally told her, "You are talking backwards, all prepared."

Mrs. High and the others then accepted the relevancy of Sally's remarks, and also Laura's derogatory ones about her mother's cooking at home. Mrs. High stated, "I try to think they have the same mechanisms we have." She told of a woman rebelling in a bridge game against Mrs. High's strict, disciplinarian husband. She thought that hostility in the football game was similar to this, that the game was forced on her.

Mrs. Springer then in general terms threatened violence to any person looking down on her. Sally stated, "I kick them back, but when I kick them back they die. . . . they are still kicking." Karen smilingly threw a book at her mother.

Mrs. High brought up Hilda's preoccupation with death during the last few months, and Sally stated, "Hilda feels her life is in danger. . . . it is not yours to say she is not tortured. . . . like an elephant never forgets. . . . and a giraffe never remembers." Mrs. High, after noting that Sally was making fun of what she was saying, and of the doctor, talked with the doctor of her own despair on being made fun of. Mrs. Knowland told Mrs. High that Hilda was more interested, and "smarter than you are."

The mother-daughter relationship sequence was complexly interwoven about the theme of being forced to do something (brought up through Sally's playing ball). The mother interpreted her daughter's behavior as related to sexual stimulation, and denied the daughter's awareness of the event. Kicking the mother back in a verbally recriminative manner occupied the latter half of the session. It became clearer that the feelings of the daughter which the mothers rejected were those which were somehow derogatory to the mothers. There was some acceptance of Sally's feelings by Mrs. High, and Karen got back at her mother by throwing a book at her.

While not crystallized as in the last session, the feeling of threat experienced by the daughter (and mother) when forced to do something was brought out, and Mrs. Springer's denial of awareness of her daughter's feelings decreased somewhat.

In the next three sessions, the mothers pushed their daughters toward giving in to their "benevolent" demands, to the daughters' resentment, and then turned around and expressed resentment of the daughters' domineering ways. There was then agreement that the anguish was shared by both. The mother as closest to the child because mother was around the most, and the child as different from an early age were then discussed. Mrs. Springer indicted most mothers as lacking proper mother-care instincts (her own ways). There was a great deal of loud protest by the mothers on their adequacy as mothers.

The issue seemed to revolve about why the daughter turned on the mother, with persistent disclosure of doubt as to whether the mothers' feelings were beneficial to the child, as Astrid, a new member of the group, along with her mother,

Mrs. Angell, pantomimed suicide, illustrating the daughter's preoccupation with death as a vengeful way out.

Session 55

Both Mrs. Knowland and Mrs. Springer spoke in general terms of their fear of rebuff. Pointing at the daughters, they defended Hilda from Mrs. High's rebuff for her monotonous mention of her brother's name. Karen laughed as Mrs. Knowland pleaded with her to use the sewing machine.

Mrs. High examined her use of activity to dispel the blues derived from frustration and hopelessness "about Hilda." Mrs. Springer stated that "stimulating" her daughter was her way out. Mrs. High disparaged Hilda's, "I want to get my life going right now," as meaningless.

Mrs. High again advocated that the daughters' defect in motivation was organic; Mrs. Knowland disputed this with Mrs. High, arguing that the daughters had "good brains to start out with." Miss Sheppard defended Hilda against Mrs. High's attack for current breaches of etiquette. Mrs. Knowland spoke in appreciation of Hilda's silences and chest banging as her way of saying unpleasant things.

Mrs. High stated she took Hilda's behavior as a sign to society that Mrs. High didn't care, and told of her own tendency to act like Hilda when she was in a bad mood. Hilda brought up her ideas of death—as a coffin, and related to "rough treatment." After Mrs. High claimed death was a mystery to them both, Hilda stated, "Yes, death is settled, . . ." and "I know all about death."

Mrs. Angell and Astrid brought out Astrid's taking on the ways of a child again, "to be happy and gay." Astrid played with paper dolls while she spoke of her advanced age, double-crossing her mother, of being "a grown-up woman who has turned herself into a child." Mrs. Angell stated, "It's confusing to me."

The preoccupation of both mother and daughter with rejection of each other came out in the interaction between Mrs. High and Hilda on the meaning Mrs. High derived from

Hilda's behavior: a sign to society that mother didn't care.

Mrs. High's important revelation seemed to lead to Hilda's statement regarding her "settled" death wishes in relation to "rough treatment."

This point in the discussion was reached in this session after consistent movement of the discussion from a general exchange on fear of rebuff to personalized statements of the defenses against such fear, their impact on the daughter, and the meaning of the daughters' (Hilda's, in this case) bizarre defenses against their own and mothers' anxiety. There was a gradually more direct exchange between Mrs. High and Hilda of each other's feelings and defenses against anxiety in their relationship. Of note was Mrs. High's reference to Hilda's behavior as a sort of rebellion and negation of her own dependent feelings. There was a matching of who knows more about death and being hurt.

The Angells broke the discussion off at the point of their mutual preoccupation, regarding suicide, with their defenses of childlike gaiety and role switching.

Session 57

Before the session started, Astrid shouted to Mrs. Angell, "Don't you match your brains with mine, ever." Hilda was lucidly independent of Mrs. High. Mrs. High brought out her comparable defenses of change of activity, and enjoyment of other people. Hilda introduced discussion of reaction to life in the hospital. Hilda told of her likes on the ward, bragged about wearing a strong (ward) dress, to Mrs. High's discomfiture. Mrs. High complained Hilda had stated she enjoyed slipping from reality. Astrid followed this up with a bitter denunciation of her mother's disavowal of complicity in her hospitalization.

When the doctor restated Mrs. High's inquiry about getting into daughter's life, Hilda asked if Mrs. High had ever been to the frigid zone. Mrs. High denied the reality of this advocated realism. Mrs. Angell noted her own wishes to daydream and read.

Mrs. Springer told of her own mental illness, with loss of interest in the things she loved and recovery on her own, despite treatment.

The question of entering into the patient's life was pursued by Mrs. Knowland and Mrs. Link as dependent on the daughter's receptivity. Both advocated that the mother hold herself in readiness rather than enter the other's life. Laura noted she had blisters inside her mouth.

At Mrs. Springer's insistence, the daughters told where they wanted to go on a trip; but Mrs. Knowland brought the discussion back to what the homes lacked. The affection which the mothers gave the daughters and the daughters' failure to respond to it were discussed.

Mrs. High stated that the daughters had grievances; she cited experiences of discomfort on receiving affection of that kind and that the affection was false. Mrs. Springer called herself an inadequate mother; Mrs. Roper said that Rae preferred her father. Mrs. Angell conjectured that Astrid refused affection because of grief, which she herself had experienced when her mother died. The group became quiet.

Overcoming this resistance was discussed next. The mothers again advocated their own defenses. Change was accomplished in the daughter by "digging it out," according to Mrs. High, who conceded helplessness in "finding a new path." Miss Sheppard recommended, "reconnecting themes." Mrs. Knowland eschewed intellectualism and spoke of "digging another path." Hilda and Astrid were vaguely bitter about hospitalization and wanted action.

In this session, Astrid and Hilda acted tough, cold, and recriminative toward their mothers about their hospitalization. The mothers sought to "enter the patients' lives" and were responded to by Hilda and by Laura. Both rejected receptivity, Laura doing so as an oral process (blisters in her mouth). The mothers exchanged mutual and self-recriminations on why their affection was not reciprocated and how they could achieve this reciprocation.

The group was closer to bridging the enormous gulf of recrimination and hatred separating mother and daughter. In this session there was evidence of mutual support and recognition on the part of the mothers and daughters as separate groups for one another. Communication between the groups became freer and clearer, although schizophrenic language and behavior were still present.

In the next few meetings, the mothers continued to mull over why their daughters were unresponsive to their show of affection and discussed ways of reaching them in a manner different from the past. They began to abandon their defenses in relation to their daughters and stated the futility of directly changing their daughters' behavior. Their daughters expressed their feelings of sadness and aloneness in an extremely impulsive, tearful and naïve fashion. Hilda came out with: "I want my years back." "I don't want death, Mother, I want to live."

Memories of the past were brought out by the daughters, with the mothers fighting awareness of them through fighting their mention by their daughters. The disjunctive phenomena of the day, such as disrobing, scratching self, masturbating, were more often tied to some feeling the daughter had about her current or past mode of living. The mothers' hostility took very open form and they began showing a decrease in their compulsion to visit their daughters.

The focus began shifting from Mrs. High and Hilda to Mrs. Springer and Sally, and then to Mrs. Angell and Astrid. Sally furiously attacked her mother for her attentiveness to her, and spoke of her own despondency and bitterness, "You reach out and the black sky falls on you." Hilda and Rae spoke of their need for love, Rae attributing her illness to the death of her grandmother. Hilda wanted to be carried, and asked the doctor for help with her problem.

Mrs. High spoke of Hilda's aggressive motions, "They

must have something to do with relationships, because they frighten people." Mrs. High, early in the therapy, with the implicit approval of other mothers, had attacked the patients' mode of communicating as being childish. She had insisted, in a number of meetings, that Hilda speak her language. She now attempted to understand Hilda's strange speech. When Hilda mentioned oatmeal or eating spaghetti, Mrs. High interpreted that she wanted to change the subject.

The mothers discussed the wall between themselves and the patients, and their self-reproaches for their failure with them. The wall was shaken some more when Mrs. High was consoled by Astrid as kind, and Laura struck Mrs. Angell.

Session 58

Hilda told Mrs. High that she had no saliva, "all used up, and can't live without it," and Mrs. High stated Hilda did have saliva. After this interchange each patient showed feeling characteristically: Karen was bright and hopeful, Sally sad and angry, Astrid bitter, and Rae annoyed.

Mrs. Knowland stated Karen was more interested in things. Mrs. High related that Hilda told her she was fantasying when she talked of Dr. Fine, and mentioned her own past fantasy of Hilda as a doctor. Hilda became restless and Karen masturbated.

Mrs. Springer told of her fantasy of Sally as a movie star. Sally spoke in a vague, sarcastic manner. Mrs. High and Miss Sheppard criticized Mrs. Springer's ambition for Sally: "too high star," and "making fun of her." The mothers alluded to this daughter as the one they had particular dreams and ambitions for and to their disappointments.

When the mothers urged their favorite activities—psychodrama, sewing, dancing, music—on their daughters, Mrs. High complained of Hilda's lack of initiative, "there is only a fantasy uppermost in her mind."

Astrid, in reply to her mother's question as to what she wanted to do, stated she wanted to commit suicide. The mothers, shocked, all urged their daughters to talk to the doctor. Mrs. High and Mrs. Springer commented on the ugliness of this hospital. Mrs. High found the beauty of Sheppard Pratt Hospital ineffective.

Hilda cried, moved to bite her mother's hand, and with anguish called, "I don't want to be dead." Her crying grew stronger as she saw the tears of her mother, and she asked if "dead people had their eyes open or closed?" Astrid threw an orange to Mrs. High for Hilda. Hilda cried, "I want my years back," and her mother, also crying said, "I know what she means."

Hilda impulsively sat on the doctor's lap and Mrs. High urged, "He will help you." Hilda stated she wanted her "1947 back," and Mrs. High said she couldn't have it back. Hilda asked if she would "promise 1950." "I don't want death, Mother, I want to live." The meeting ended with Hilda crying in a childish, spasmodic way.

In this session there was, on the issue brought on by mother's wish for daughter to do something, clearer communication by daughter to mother of her underlying feelings of abandonment and of preoccupation with death. The daughters also indirectly indicated their positive wishes through action and symbolic representation.

There was a great deal of interchange between mothers on their fantasies and defenses in the group, notably Mrs. High and Mrs. Springer (especially in Mrs. Springer's ambitions for Sally). These fantasies seemed to be projections onto the daughters of unrealized personal ambitions. The daughters reinforced one another in expression of feelings. Astrid, by throwing the symbolically meaningful orange, expressed her warm feeling and desire to console; in other contests, where she was directly more dependent on her mother, she manifested instead a destructive competitiveness. An example of this was her competitive rejection of mother in the very beginning of Session 57.

Session 61

Hilda asked for "cold medicine," as her mother spoke of Hilda's threats to scratch her face. She then pointed out the self-inflicted scratches on her face as her mother badgered her to use Kleenex tissue properly, and said, "garbage can." Mrs. High understood this to mean "put in the garbage can." Miss Sheppard appreciated the appropriateness of Tina's laughter at this point.

Mrs. High described her own incessant probing, and the way she and Hilda "chased around each other's tails." As she bitterly complained that her visiting Hilda less often had not helped Hilda, Hilda introduced the phrase, "life on an ocean wave." The doctor called for interpretations of this phrase. After initial resistance to accepting it as having any meaning, members of the group interpreted it to mean freedom, happiness, gaiety.

Hilda, at Mrs. High's insistence, told that its meaning involved surgeons, a dark-haired and dark-eyed woman, of liking a male doctor and china plates better than tin plates (she ate on one in the cafeteria, in contrast to china at home). Hilda told herself to forget tin plates and hospital personnel because of her death, but since "the cemetery is not important," suggested "we talk about the doctor, more important." Mrs. High interpreted first that the people mentioned obstructed Hilda's getting to the crest of the wave, then that Hilda's life was a weary seasickness.

When Miss Sheppard pointed out the life-threatening character of life on an ocean wave, Mrs. High dismissed the expression as "trash." Later she showed anger at the doctor, and resistance and despair about understanding further. She stated that it was "all Hilda's own doing." Hilda clearly stated to her mother, "I am not paying attention," when Mrs. High insisted that Hilda verbalize only in her mother's way.

Attentive to the meaning her daughter attempted to convey to her, and at the same time as expressing her own feelings, Mrs. High came to understand Hilda's statement of "garbage can," and with the group's help some of the meaning of "life on an ocean wave." She resisted its deeper implications, pertinent to the death wishes brought up in earlier sessions, and despairingly put the blame on Hilda. Hilda retaliated with, "I am not paying attention."

Sessions 62-64

The resentment of the mothers at exclusion from daughter's world, and of the daughter at mother's overprotectiveness and forcing of compliance were again brought out. Mrs. Knowland and Mrs. High attacked Mrs. Angell for her overprotectiveness, and Mrs. Angell in turn blamed Astrid's paternal grandmother for giving Astrid "ideas and airs about herself." Mrs. Knowland blamed Mrs. Angell's protectiveness on her dislike of the daughter's personality, because Astrid, the "sporty, cool type," resembled her first husband, Astrid's father. She claimed that the patients rejected the kind of mothering given to them when father rejected mother.

Mrs. High was proud of her ability to stand up to him when he ridiculed her for taking Hilda too seriously. In a derogatory way she brought out his romantic dream of a farm, which she thought was an escape comparable to Hilda's "private romances." Astrid attacked her mother as "insane" and as having sexual relations with a dog. Hilda attacked her mother as a "dead cow."

The mothers went further into their ambivalent attachment to daughter. The relationship of mother to husband and her own mother was broached, with rejection of the child as related to rejection of and by husband and mother. Untouched was the need to appease the demanding husband and grandmother who represented the mother's own internalized demands on herself. Mrs. High's assertion of her independence here was apparently an effort at therapeutic movement.

Open, vaguely competitive conflict was revealed between Mrs. High and her husband, with Hilda and his farm as each other's escape from the anxiety in their relationship. The daughters in a derogatory manner pointed to the mothers' sexual relationship to husband.

Session 65

Pushing the daughter to "natural" activities and hobbies predetermined by the mother's interests gave way to questioning by the mothers of all the daughters on what they wanted, with Karen reporting that she wanted a shop of her own, and Hilda "my years back." The group discussed social action on the part of the mothers in reference to the hospital, going into the effects of hospitalization on the mothers, with Mrs. Link telling of her "broken heart," and Astrid, "It knocks you for a loop. These people over here aren't as crazy as you are."

Session 66

Open statement was made of recognition of the futility of changing daughter's and the ward group's patterns of behavior and restraint. Mrs. High wished to make amends and Mrs. Knowland emphasized the daughters' need for approval and freedom to experiment. Astrid spoke of being given things and knocked down and of getting mother's goat, "I have a stick and I have skates. I hold onto it when I go skating."

Sessions 67–69

Mrs. High and Hilda took a central position in these meetings. Mrs. High accepted Hilda's "feeling buffeted around," "like a midget," "cripple who can't walk and wishes to be carried," and "dead pigeon off the streets," but she still maintained that Hilda should have defenses like her own. Hilda mimicked her mother, but turned on herself and tore her dress methodically. Bluntly, when Mrs. High noted that her family was blunt, Hilda characterized herself as a worthless piece of wood. She repeatedly mentioned that she was thinking of the cemetery and that she had buried her shoes.

In the next session, both Astrid and Sally turned furiously on their mothers who were pressing them to conformity through interest in things, with statements like, "You locked me in jail and left me" (Astrid), and "Get off my back, you fucking idiot. You are like living, hopeless beings. You're dying" (Sally). Mrs. High criticized Mrs. Springer's handling of Sally like a little child. The daughters also came out with more data on mother killing father.

Sally's despair was discussed in the next session, and she stated, "You reach out and the black sky falls on you." *Mrs. High and the group attempted to track down why Hilda angrily and defiantly tore her dress, and traced it to despair starting a half hour before, related to her being "heartbroken when her mother doesn't come."* Sally and Astrid spoke of love, and Astrid said, "It's a terrible thing to destroy anybody's heart."

After Mrs. Roper stated, "That's what they do to us," Rae told of having no mother and of being very upset when grandmother died. Again, the resentment of daughter against correction, isolation from home, and rigid expectations was expressed.

The group's ability to trace back the onset of the anxiety and anger in the interaction of the Highs was a significant indication in the members' growth of ego strength in the group situation. It was also indicative of a greater degree of contact with the reality of the group situation.

The close relationship of daughter with grandmother, broached earlier in the Angells' participation, as a genetic factor in daughter's illness, was indicated in Rae's statement about not having any mother and her upset when grandmother died. Mrs. Roper's tendency to abdicate her responsibility as a mother was apparent in the group in her obeisance to the doctor, group members, and daughter.

Session 70

Hilda, after the group had complimented her on having been a gracious hostess at her recent birthday party, asked for help with her problem, "Carry me, I can't walk. . . . I am through menstruating. Dead people don't menstruate, do they?" She then withdrew from further discussion.

The mothers discussed criticism first as an appreciation of their daughters. Then Mrs. Springer and Mrs. High brought out their own sensitivity to criticism. Mrs. Angell was revealed to have been hospitalized the previous week in one of the local hospitals for a "heart attack." This was thought of as emotional by Mrs. High.

Sessions 71–72

Conformity to standards was discussed in these sessions as propensities more of the middle class and of men; women were described as more warmhearted and tender. Mrs. Knowland advocated accepting the patients, and stated her displeasure at Karen's trying to please her in order to stay at home.

The wall between self and daughter was agreed on by Mrs. High and Mrs. Roper and both reproached themselves for their failure in bringing up their daughters. Astrid consoled Mrs. High as kind.

There was a softening of the "masculine" tendency of the mothers to require conformity of their daughters. It became apparent that they were beginning to face dependent aspects of their relationship with husband, in regard to their need for love and support. They seemed to have turned to competitive masculine ways and to a dependent relationship on a child. The child was seen as both rebellious and hopelessly infantile and inadequate.

Sessions 73–74

Mrs. Knowland pressed her attack on the mothers as not wanting to change, and as having their minds in a rut. In the next session, Mrs. Tenant reported a change in Tina, in that she cried for her father when Mrs. High visited her.

Laura gratefully told the doctor how he had helped her get her feelings back, and now all she had to do was to get herself under control. Mrs. Link was attacked by Mrs. Knowland for insisting that Laura be sweet and do nothing. Mrs. Link tearfully told of her desperate feeling that she was cheating on Laura, who liked her father. Mrs. Tenant was moved to tell of Tina's inability to communicate, but her facility in understanding what was going on.

Change in the mother was characteristically mentioned in reference first to change in the daughter, this time in Tina's change in wanting her father. Mrs. Link's awareness of impending closeness in the relationship of her daughter and husband also came out.

Laura was the first of the patients with whom the doctor achieved a relationship on a give-and-take, ego level. In this session she acknowledged a real dependency on the doctor for help, and simultaneously assumed greater responsibility for her own feelings, in speaking of control of her own feelings. Hitherto, this was of some importance as an issue in the group, inasmuch as control had been broached through the question of controlling the other.

Session 75

There was intense discussion of the issue of control, with the mothers appraising its uses. Mrs. High appealed to the doctor to control her so that she would stop going around in circles. She and Mrs. Knowland talked of the need to control feelings, Mrs. Knowland describing the danger of what might happen if the "dam should break."

The mothers shifted from controlling others to the issue of controlling themselves; and this was the prelude to their gradually revealing their own unacceptable feelings of anger and resentment in later meetings.

Sessions 76–77

The discussion of control continued and went on to the feelings the mothers had when the patients lost control. During this session, Laura struck Mrs. Angell "for getting in front of my mother." Mrs. Angell irritably maintained that her reaction was not anger at the blow as was evident to group members and the doctor, but fright. Laura's blow at Mrs. Angell was a mock attack, deeply ambivalent, in which she made fun of and protected her mother. Laura was perhaps expressing openly her own competitiveness through action on behalf of her mother.

In the next session, Mrs. Angell's feelings last time were brought up. Although she continued to deny anger, others, especially Mrs. Springer and Mrs. Knowland, admitted getting angry at their daughters when the daughters lost control. Mrs. High spoke of being "angry and ashamed of it." The mothers felt the need of control, and Mrs. Springer said she learned control by watching Sally. They talked of daughters' resistance to doing what they were told, such as bathing or eating.

Mrs. High sadly connected Hilda's mention of cemeteries with the futility of her existence.

The mothers chided themselves for babying their daughters, Mrs. Angell saying that since Astrid was ill, she couldn't help it. Astrid responded, "This is your punishment for being so guilty."

By this point in the group the mothers were on the verge of expressing a negative reaction to the immediate group situation, that is, to describing the immediate interpersonal situation. The mothers continued to identify more readily with the daughters.

Session 78

Initial expressions of discouragement were followed by Mrs. High's statement to Mrs. Springer, "If you didn't feel there might be some hope, you wouldn't come to these meetings," and Hilda, "I want to get well." Mrs. Angell told of Astrid's improvement. Astrid said, "I don't know who you are, but you are the only person who understands poor Astrid." As Mrs. Angell assured her of warmth and affection, Astrid said, "Astrid doesn't care what you say . . . . she has a certain boundary line in the world." Astrid looked distressed and left the meeting. The discussion moved to the effect of early trauma, and Mrs. Springer told of being upset while nursing Sally. Hilda referred to Astrid stating, "she's constipated."

Mrs. Angell was less controlling, and Astrid recognized her empathy, but was not yet ready to accept her mother's affection; she rejected it with her delineation of a "boundary line."

Sessions 79–80

Mrs. High, distraught, attacked a letter Hilda had written because of its discontinuity and apparent lack of meaning. The doctor took the lead in explaining its coherence, and Mrs. Springer defended Hilda's feelings as valid. She explained Hilda's anger as bringing her closer to people, and that one associates every irritation with mother, "the one nearest to you." Both Mrs. Angell and Mrs. High told of the improvement in their daughters' behavior, Astrid showing less intensity and frequency of furious, wild behavior, and Hilda showing "more sense to what she was doing," and greater "feeling for human beings."

Mrs. Angell and Mrs. Knowland claimed that the grandmother was partly responsible for the daughters' antagonistic behavior.

Session 81

Rae refused to attend the meeting. Hilda started the meeting by telling the doctor, "I'm facing life"; and her mother stated, "I don't know what to lean on."

Mrs. Springer reproved Mrs. High for addressing the patients as children, and Astrid told her mother, "I have never been so humiliated." The mothers expressed bewilderment when a visiting patient remarked that their daughters were better when the mothers didn't visit.

Amid the rising tension over this, Astrid swore and threw banana skins on the floor. Mrs. Angell could acknowledge only affection, but admitted she would have other feelings at home.

There was discussion of the mothers' humiliation in this situation, as well as the daughters'. Mrs. Springer noted how the daughters bullied their mothers.

Feelings of humiliation were now related to behavior: by the daughters to mother's babying, and by the mothers to the daughter's misbehavior.

Session 82

The mothers told of their feelings of worrying too much (Mrs. Tenant), being human and angry (Mrs. Angell), being confused and treating Hilda as a child (Mrs. High) and of getting down to their daughters' level. Astrid said, "You certainly do"; and Sally, "It means that there is a beginning of spring, doesn't it?"

Hilda, under attack by her mother and defended by Mrs. Springer, said she didn't feel like explaining her words.

Mrs. Roper said she realized that smoking, a permanent point of issue between Rae and herself, was just a manifestation of Rae's illness.

Mrs. Knowland brought out that this was an aspect of the conflict between Mrs. Roper and her husband. Mrs. Roper denied this, but described "going to pieces" last Wednesday in a conflict with him. Astrid thereupon described her own toughness and cruelty.

All the mothers joined in expressing their depressed feeling, "worse than losing someone" when they left their daughters in the hospital.

They also expressed restrained bitterness toward their husbands who, in their "realism," were doubting and derogatory about the mothers' dreams for their daughters. Mrs. High stated, "Hilda is doing to me what I do to Mr. High." Astrid commented, "Making fun of people is the greatest pleasure for some people."

Having relinquished some control over their daughters and over unacceptable feelings, the mothers declared themselves to be on a level with the daughters. This was greeted by the daughters as a hopeful ("beginning of spring") sign.

The daughter's place, as a bone of contention between mother and father, emerged more clearly. Further revelation occurred of the grief-laden connotation to leaving daughter, and of her retributive abandonment of her derogatory husband, doing to husband as daughter did to her.

Session 83

Mr. High died several days after the bitter outburst of the last session "of a thrombosis, not a heart attack," Mrs. High was reported to have stated. The mothers displayed intense resentment toward authority figures in the hospital for what they characterized as its nonresponsiveness to their suggestions, and the torture they underwent visiting their daughters, who presented them only with boredom. On the other hand, they showed sympathy for their husbands as not crying but still taking it more seriously than the mothers thought.

Astrid alternately threatened to beat up her mother and cried about being beloved by a boy friend, and her inability to take her mind off him. Mrs. Roper reported Rae as increasingly sulky and unresponsive to herself and warm to her father. Hilda referred to herself as full of prunes and belching, a remark related to constipation and inability to express her feelings.

The death of Mr. High seemed to have been presaged by vague thoughts on his departure for some time. Mrs. High apparently linked heart attack with emotional difficulties— Mrs. Angell had a "heart attack" which Mrs. High had "seen through" as emotional. The mothers characteristically at this point turned on the hospital authorities and their daughters for their nonresponsiveness, as they had on their husbands, and for the while looked on their husbands as caring.

Astrid seemed to be giving her version of this recriminative turning to another for care. Mrs. Roper despairingly spoke of Rae's approach to herself and her husband. Hilda hinted at her holding in her feelings anally, and belching.

The mothers exercised control of their feelings through attentiveness away from themselves, onto the hospital and their daughters. This question of who exerts control was further explored in the next session.

Session 85

The question of who had the upper hand in the situation was brought up by Astrid who stated that she was raised like cattle, and these people conquered her like a beast, that the patients had the upper hand in the hospital, and that nothing influenced her but herself. Sally agreed. Mrs. Roper stated that Rae had the upper hand in regard to discipline. Mrs. High was contrite with reference to nagging Hilda, "I can't stop it though I try," and Astrid stated, "They will continue to nag, while we are insane."

Session 86

The mothers agreed that it was their task to find out what was wrong with themselves as mothers. Mrs. Tenant expressed guilt about not sending Tina off to a private school sooner, but was upset by Tina's nonresponsiveness in regard to conformity.

Mrs. Link told how Laura soiled her bed and smeared herself and mother, but Mrs. Link could feel no anger, only love. Mrs. Angell felt the same way to Astrid, and the mothers agreed they had to give the daughters anything they asked for.

Laura consoled her mother, "Don't you feel bad." Astrid mentioned, "revenge." Mrs. Knowland told of saying nasty things to Karen when Karen turned away from her. Rae provoked her mother by attempting to love a hospital aide at the meeting.

Hilda spoke of being constipated, and said she was "not afraid of enemas. . . . I want to set the clock back."

Mrs. Springer and Mrs. Angell expressed a new realization and appreciation that their daughters could be worse, but were not. Mrs. Roper and Mrs. Springer implied resentment at their daughters for failure to see them. Mrs. Roper said Rae slammed the door in her face.

Mrs. Angell expressed the complaint, "If I look back, I will get sick." Astrid told of her problem in life as not being able to keep her mind off her boy friend, and accused her mother of guilt and defending herself against some anticipated accusation. She saw a "silver lining coming up" in her mother's "guilty face," but didn't care. Mrs. Knowland attacked Mrs. Tenant for not believing Tina had capacity for growth.

In these sessions, there was a crescendo of revelation of resentment toward the behavior of the daughters, with some mothers continuing to deny a resentful reaction, but others admitting it. After the shock of Mr. High's death, the mothers and daughters were again inquiring into themselves through the group discussion. Her mother's sense of guilt was brought up by Astrid and the question of what they pay attention to to keep from experiencing anxiety came out further in the mothers' reference to not looking back. Hilda's acceptance of an enema (of psychotherapy, cf. Session 6, in which she had preferred electroshock to the enema of psychotherapy) was significant. She was willing to accept help in working through recriminative aspects of her relationships. Astrid's stated problem in life of not being able to take her mind off her boy friend and preoccupation with her father's family kept uncovering Mrs. Angell's past marital relationship and emotional investments.

The daughters' feelings about mothers' protectiveness, chiefly expressed by Astrid and Hilda, and the mothers' guilt and sense of hopelessness and failure expressed by Mrs. Angell and Mrs. Springer, gained gradually clearer and stronger expression in the next seven sessions. Astrid related her hopeless vengefulness toward mother for putting her in the hospital and Mrs. Angell her abject guilt in reference to not meeting Astrid's immediate needs.

Session 88

Laura's hopeless depression, Hilda's toughness and fear, Astrid's murderous and suicidal feelings, and need for tenderness and trust, and Tina's lack of understanding and perceptiveness were brought out in relation to their mothers. When Mrs. Tenant insisted that Tina needed childhood surroundings to be happy, Astrid commented, "I will be happy when they put me in a play-pen and it is all over." When Mrs. Angell insisted she had to show she is well, she replied, "I see what you mean, Hilda; I have the same problem in my life. I would like to kill her."

Mrs. High then brought out her self-reproach and punish-ment as not different from Hilda's, illustrating with her own re-cent nail biting and eating all day, and that through trouble you get better understanding.

When Mrs. Angell stated that she couldn't stand anger in others, Hilda stated "Logic." Mrs. Angell went on to tell of As-trid's ability to "hold it in" when her maternal grandmother died. Astrid then commented on herself as a boy acting like a girl.

On a rising note of mutuality, Hilda, in contrast to a pre-vious expression of discouragement with it, told Mrs. Tenant of the good qualities of the private school she had gone to, and Mrs. Tenant talked of Tina's increasing power of communication.

Astrid in the session commented on Mrs. Tenant's and her own mother's controlling behavior toward Tina and her-self, and on her own resultant murderous feelings. Mrs. High came out further with her own depressive experiences and her similarity to Hilda.

Mrs. Angell's intolerance of feelings in others, and her comment on Astrid's control resulted in Astrid's mention of her characteristic role-playing mechanism (similar to Hilda's acting like a tough insensitive boy).

Session 89

Mrs. Springer encouraged expression of feeling in the form of crying. Astrid stated that deep in her heart a home belonged to her, and told of the alternatives of going to grandmother when things were not nice at home, and if they were not nice there, running away. Mrs. Angell described her own mother as overstrict on sex, and asserted a mother shouldn't impose herself on her child. Then she spoke of the helplessness of the patients, and how they needed control. Astrid stated sarcastically, "They may jump out of the Empire State Building and hurt themselves."

Session 91

The mothers recognized the oppositional defiance of their daughters as a defense against mother. Karen read someone else's magazine in defiance of mother's proscription. Hilda spoke of "other people" and cemeteries. Astrid called Mrs. High, to whom she had sent a valentine, "grandmother." Mrs. High and Mrs. Springer commented on the daughters' lacking the tact to protect the feelings of others.

Mrs. Springer compared herself to Sally in her misery-driven wild assaultiveness, with, "If I had been a man, I would have been a fighter—not taken anything off of anybody." This led to Mrs. Angell's description of her own angry feeling, like "banging the walls if no one saw, let loose," when she couldn't have Astrid home for the week end. Astrid then stated, "And cry about your mother's death."

Mrs. Angell opposed idolizing a child; and Astrid spoke of having her own bed, being alone, and loved. Mrs. Angell then reported dreaming of people who were dead, just before Astrid got sick; Astrid added to this that her mother ought to get her nose busted.

Session 92

The meeting opened with a display of hostility between Astrid and Laura and a statement by Hilda about sticking a pin in her foot. After talking of sex, coupled with violence and death, Astrid came out with, "and come to the conclusion you want to commit suicide and don't know how." Hilda stated, "The sky is green, isn't it?"

Astrid cried, and her mother reported Astrid's recent statement that it was inconceivable to her that she was in the hospital. Astrid replied, "It is a safe place to stay." Mrs. Angell and Mrs. Springer looked on the patients as more miserable than the mothers. They and Mrs. Roper joined in attacking the hospital as not caring and being careless.

Astrid referred to herself as a young man, who could have all the girls she wanted (a Don Juan in a harem role she played on the ward) and wouldn't do any more for mother, "because you stink to me." The mothers disputed over whether Astrid meant it, with Mrs. Knowland holding she did. Ronnie, a visiting patient, told of the relative desirability of the life of a prostitute, even with its morbid "slain in the bathtub" end; she described despondency as nothing but agitation about a new house (the future).

The daughters' masochistic aggressivity toward their mothers as a form of recrimination for their hospitalization came out again and more openly this session through the statements of Hilda, Astrid and Ronnie, with Astrid as a central figure. The mothers related to the hospital authorities on much the same level.

Session 93

After Mrs. High happily reported that Hilda was showing displeasure over some incongruous features of her own behavior, Hilda dutifully reported that Astrid was on the warpath. Mrs. Knowland commented that forgetting without understanding is futile. Astrid came out with a long speech, taking the form of an admonition by an older person to a younger one to "show them" things. She told herself things which produced pride and others humiliation. The proud data had to do with other people being like animals; the need to show the prettier side; one can fight back; showing respect for the opposite sex. The humiliating data were on self as crazy; can't control one's emotions; can't keep pants on; self as Hitler, as queer. "Show them you hate them, no matter how sexy you get, you don't care." Mrs. Springer claimed Astrid was "bolstering herself against fear, in which state everybody is like a monster." Mrs. Angell stated that Astrid had an inferiority complex, to which Astrid replied, "And if you have it, don't show it."

Astrid bitterly hurled back her mother's exhortations to be proud and to repress or avoid what was humiliating. This led directly to the interaction which followed in the next two sessions.

Session 95

Astrid spoke of Rae as having an inferiority complex, to cover up her body, "making herself like the rest of the girls, with lipstick." Mrs. Springer, acknowledging her own feelings of inferiority, said they were caused by the expectation of failure; and Mrs. Knowland commented on that factor as making Astrid feel inferior or "awful strong." Karen then forcefully grabbed a magazine from Hilda.

Mrs. Springer and Mrs. Roper spoke of their daughters' helplessness, and of how nothing could relieve them "until the pressure is relieved first." Astrid contemplatively stated, "I don't know, but it has been in my head ever since I have been born." Mrs. Springer voiced the feelings of the mothers that they were trapped. Astrid spoke excitedly of a roller-coaster and Hilda of constipation. Mrs. Springer said she thought people who had worked here for years would wish that there would be an earthquake, and everything would drop down in, and of one through stupidity, destroying a whole world. The mothers attempted to speak in a less morbid vein, but Mrs. Springer continued to talk about how the patients had decayed. Astrid (whose mother was absent today) stated, "I know my mother wants me to die." After being assured by others that her mother loved her, Astrid talked about herself. She said she was a big girl when her mother got married to the German army, that she was unkind and different from the rest of the family, turning against them, that she smiled very hard to be beautiful, and was capable as a child. She talked of mother's hypocrisy, sarcastically mentioning her solicitude. When the doctor said to Astrid, "You feel that your mother doesn't care as much as Mrs. Tenant," Mrs. Tenant quickly spoke up to Astrid reassuringly, and anxiously, "Yes, she does! She called me up, and told me to curl your hair tomorrow." Various mothers made sympathetic comments to Astrid. Astrid said clearly and despondently, "I know my mother doesn't care. She wants me to die." Mrs. Roper said, "Oh no, she loves you, Astrid." Rae laughed.

Astrid stated, "At the end of the day you feel like you want to die, when you feel you don't love mother and father any more; feel righteous; to go to the basement and rollerskate." Mrs. Springer said to Astrid, "At the end of the day you feel low." Astrid retorted, "At the end of the day you feel like committing suicide. I don't know how to express my feelings." Mrs. Springer spoke sympathetically. Astrid went on talking rapidly and incoherently and spoke of scramming.

Mrs. Springer and Mrs. Knowland called for comment from Astrid relative to the feelings of the daughters, and listened intently to her denunciations.

At the outset Astrid broached her "inferiority complex" by referring to Rae, an act of attention to a quality she and Rae shared. The preoccupation with self as a boy was touched on.

The mothers supplied associations to Astrid's presenting complaint from their own experiences—especially Mrs. Springer, whose psychosis had involved acute "expectation of failure." Mrs. Knowland's power struggles were reflected in her "awful strong" statement.

Karen followed this reference to strength by a forceful display of willfulness, as if it were a command from mother.

The next point, the need for relief of the patient through dealing with the internal pressure (localized in her head as present since birth by Astrid) as opposed to outside activities, came as a surprise, since Mrs. Springer had formerly proposed sunbathing in the nude, freer sex life, etc., as the cure.

Loss of control in this session began when Mrs. Springer expressed the mothers' feeling of being trapped. This brought out the feelings of Astrid and Hilda, and Mrs. Springer's death wishes toward the entire institution.

Thereupon followed the eruption of Astrid's feelings.

This interaction, while apparently genuine enough, and extremely moving to all participants in it, was not fully in a reality context; i.e., there was no agreed-upon immediate interpersonal issue that it devolved upon to fix it in reality for the participants. In the next, the last observed session, such an issue appeared in the form of Astrid's forthcoming birthday party. This event was of some importance in the group, since it had become a custom for such parties to be held. In Hilda's case, it had been held at Mrs. Knowland's home. Laura's and Rae's were held in the hospital on the ward.

Session 96

The meeting opened with the announcement that observations were being terminated; and the group responded with a genuine feeling of loss for the observer. Mrs. Knowland reported her dejection after last week's meeting. Mrs. Roper in a long statement claimed that her thoughts when depressed by not seeing Rae would not be helpful in the group. She felt helpless in not being able to do anything with Rae.

Mrs. Springer spoke of the spiritual as something she couldn't understand at all. Mrs. Knowland defined it as relationship. Mrs. Springer reported having no faith, and just having "moods, sympathy." She stated she had experienced it earlier in life without anyone to lean on. Astrid on this theme denied being a girl, "like the one who became religious at twelve." Mrs. Roper spoke of Rae's unhappiness, and her own when she saw the vacant chair at the table.

This apparently brought forth Mrs. Angell's association to Astrid's forthcoming birthday party, which became the focal point of the discussion. She pressed Astrid to state her age, and Astrid answered, "ten"; then, on further pressure, "eleven . . . . fifty-six." Astrid complained bitterly that she was "punished almost like a war criminal."

Mrs. Knowland defended Astrid as realizing more than her parent. Astrid stated, "Scarlett O'Hara doesn't like me—nobody loves me and I don't know why. . . . Why do you keep pounding on my soul? . . . You are crazy, aren't you?" as mother whined that she wanted to ascertain whether Astrid knew she was there. She threatened not to have the party for Astrid.

Mrs. Angell then asked what made Astrid so bitter, "What is she so mad about?" When Mrs. Springer stated that Astrid's mind was "off," Astrid decisively told her, "Mrs. Springer, let us think of Sally first!" The group laughed.

Astrid continued, "The Germans ordering you around, and red-headed women running after me." Mrs. Angell abjectly pleaded with Astrid to sit next to her, and said she was sorry she was late in getting here today. Astrid was furious, "You have gone completely insane, they should leave you in charge of babies instead of me." She stated she dreamed that Laura was making eyes at her and she made believe she didn't care.

When Mrs. Angell stated all she wanted was for her to be happy, Astrid answered that she didn't make her happy and that Astrid was rich. When the doctor asked her what happened to her mother when she was miserable, she replied, "I kill her!" Mrs. Angell thought Astrid might be liking to hurt her, and Astrid stated that she wanted her mother to be unhappy for having put her in the hospital.

Mrs. Springer commented on the patients as too envious; unhappy, they didn't want others to be happy. Mrs. Link reported how tickled she was over Laura's improvement in the last few weeks. Astrid stated, "You need to lump things that come through your life." Mrs. Tenant and Mrs. Roper told of what looked like the happy attachment their daughters had to attendants. Mrs. Knowland asserted Astrid was nearer well when she acted defiant.

Mrs. Angell pressed the age question again, threatening no birthday party. Astrid replied: "Kill me." Mrs. Angell was distressed: "I can't talk. . . ." She said, "It hurts that I can't reach and help her!" Sally and Tina laughed. Mrs. Angell, in tears, spoke of unhappiness as possibly not so bad, and looking on the bright side as possibly not so good. She offered Astrid some cakes. Astrid answered, "You finally got around to giving me some cakes."

Mrs. Springer spoke of the patients as "dreaming things the mother can't find out," and as "bitter, venomous, and lost. Rage and spit of contempt go hand in hand with them . . . . horrible feeling."

Mrs. Knowland noted she had venom only to herself, and that "we want to reach them only on our terms." Mrs. Springer stated, "I would like to reach them in any way."

The feeling of loss on the observer's leaving expressed by the group seemed genuine. Mrs. Knowland's report on her dejection after last week's meeting was of considerable interest; apparently her control by "beaming instead of mourning" had lessened. The next communication, in tune with Mrs. Knowland, was the revelation, by Mrs. Roper, of something besides her usual report of depression, a step others had followed in the group prior to coming out with concrete destructive wishes. Actually, in the group, she had increasingly displayed hostile postural tensions, as Rae mockingly turned from her to make homosexual love to an attendant.

Mrs. Springer's reference to the spiritual was not merely coincidental. Mrs. Roper had all along referred to the "Lord's will," and also Mrs. Springer had been accused by the other mothers of being hard-hearted, not giving in to a power outside herself. Mrs. Knowland's emphasis on interpersonal "relationship" was her secular version of the spiritual. Her postural tensions and attitudes had denoted, especially at the inception of therapy, obeisance to a spiritual leader.

Mrs. Springer's subjective states of dependent "moods, or sympathy" were manifested in the group as extremely rapid and brief excursions from her affectless chirruping state, where she seemed to empathize and suffer at the moment with the sick daughter, at first Hilda, then Astrid. These "moods" became more frequent and prolonged, and may have in effect constituted a reliving of her psychosis of early adulthood.

Astrid's denial of the spiritual was tied up in the session with denying having those moods, with being a girl. On the ward she behaved generally like a boy in her homosexual interactions, acting the role of a Don Juan in a harem. At the same time she mocked femininity by painting herself flamboyantly with lipstick.

Mrs. Roper's association to unhappiness as connected with the chair empty because of Rae's absence was evidence of a mutual preoccupation of mother and daughter over their home, with considerable sharing of idealization of it, and the feeling of abandonment each experienced in relation to the other, leaving the chair empty.

In the ensuing interaction between Astrid and Mrs. Angell, both became deeply engrossed in a struggle based on an immediate problem, the birthday party. However, this involved issues pertinent to an earlier period in their lives. Involved in the issue of Astrid's statement of her age were, among other things, Mrs. Angell's motives in keeping daughter a baby. In this, Mrs. Angell was at the moment bringing into view a problem all the mothers had to some degree, of fixedly seeing the daughter. This turning to daughter as a baby rather than as a girl of fifteen seemed to be related to Mrs. Angell's problems in maintaining her identity as a mother. When Astrid did not respond properly and adequately, Mrs. Angell regressed.

Mrs. Angell's attention was centered on this, and Astrid's reply was her characteristic negativistic game-playing one. Mother centered her attention on the issue of daughter's happiness, diverting the two of them from coming to grips with their original conflict. At the end of the meeting, mother was able to relinquish this defense, and come closer to facing the painful feelings involved. Expecting punishment, which mother promptly began to mete out in the form of a pathetic look, Astrid referred to herself as a war criminal, possibly associated with mother's derogatory reference to her actual father as a German.

The mothers repeatedly had demonstrated to them in

the group the appropriateness and perspicacity of the daughters in their interaction with their relatively blind, but self-
righteous parents. This, Mrs. Knowland reflected in her reference to Astrid as knowing more than Mrs. Angell. Scarlett
O'Hara was an enthusiasm of the play-acting of Astrid and
Mrs. Angell, and here referred evidently to Mrs. Angell. Mrs.
Angell's whine relative to her daughter's expostulation was
in contrast to her self-confident attitude forty sessions ago. At
that time she was devotedly superioristic toward the sick non-
sense her daughter expressed. The question of whether Astrid
was here (in the hospital, in reality) seemed to be realized
better by Astrid than by Mrs. Angell. Back of this question
was the problem of control—if you didn't knuckle under you
would not get a birthday party because you were crazy and
could be abandoned here. This aspect was implicit in the tone
rather than in the words. Other mothers had come out openly
with this threat in earlier meetings. Another aspect of this
problem was Mrs. Angell's anxiety relative to being abandoned. She wanted to know if Astrid was there, clung to her,
and avidly asked for response by Astrid. The fact that Astrid's
full caring was rejective was incidental to Mrs. Angell's request, which was based on extremely immediate goal seeking.

Astrid's retort to Mrs. Springer on thinking of Sally first
was what Scarlett O'Hara would have done, and was a demonstration of the mechanism present in the group of "coming
up for air," which lent security to the proceedings, since the
members had some assurance they wouldn't get hopelessly lost
in subjectivity.

Mrs. Angell reverted to her pleading and placating ways
again. The sequence with daughter was repeated, with a little
more resolution of the issue of whether the mother and
daughter would abandon each other. The control of both in
the situation had been altered so that they went through their

hostility and recrimination more as revelations and confessions than as despairing sadomasochistic performances.

Mrs. Springer commented understandingly on Astrid's motive for making mother unhappy. Mrs. Link associated to the word "happy" and told of Laura's improvement. Astrid by this time had become largely contemplative, a state somewhat new to her.

The next association to "happy," that of the daughters' attachment to attendants—with overtly homosexual manifestations on the part of the daughters—presaged attack on the daughters as defiantly abandoning mother. Mrs. Knowland supported Astrid's defiance.

Mrs. Angell, again abstracted, became dependently attentive in the face of Astrid's pointed intransigeance ("Kill me") to her daughter again. She relinquished this shortly when the absurdity of her demands was pointed up by the group's withdrawal from her, punctuated by Sally's and Tina's laughter. Mrs. Angell then gave evidence of relinquishing her defense of displaying happiness, which had kept them from meaningful emotional communication for many years.

Astrid's philosophical approach was adopted by Mrs. Angell, and she freely offered the cakes. Astrid's tone in accepting them was somewhat sarcastic, but also much softer than previously when accepting food from mother.

In the last exchange between Mrs. Springer and Mrs. Knowland, there was recognition of the tendency to reach daughter only on mother's terms, and some relinquishment of this mechanism which presaged therapeutic movement.

This session was markedly different from the first one in this study in that:

(1) The doctor was more in the background, as a guide, and the projections onto him were considered as part of the analytic situation, to be investigated in the

unique manner evolved collaboratively by this group and the doctor.

(2) The group took up issues pertinent to its problems.

(3) The group took up issues pertinent to its immediate reality.

(4) The group accepted wide ranges of opinions and attitudes.

(5) The group was capable of returning to areas of conflict when anxiety of the individual sidetracked the discussion.

(6) The members were more tolerant of deep anxiety in the group setting.

(7) There was a minimum of intellectualizing.

(8) The mothers and daughters, participating as members of the same group, talked of the same issues and responded with appropriate affect.

IV

SUMMARY OF THE DEVELOPMENT OF THE GROUP AND THE MOTHER-DAUGHTER RELATIONSHIP

1. INTRODUCTION

In this chapter the data and interpretative comments presented in the preceding chapter have been gone over in an attempt further to define the patterns of relationship and development present in the group and its components. After a general historical survey, the group has been scrutinized as a dynamism. Then one of the most arresting of the phenomena which appeared in the course of the group—namely, the relationship sequence of the mother-daughter pairs—has been delineated. The participation of the professional participants in the group process, the doctor and the observer, has been subjected to scrutiny as it related to the dynamic development of the group.

2. HISTORICAL SURVEY

Introductory Phase—Sessions 1–4

At the inception of the group the immediate issues were relative to purposes and procedure. The mothers and daughters approached this problem with their usual defenses, which showed in individuals and in mother-daughter pairs. Though the mothers expressed the attitude of "I don't know anything, you tell me, doctor," it soon developed that their behavior ranged from "It's up to me to get her to change" (Mrs. High) to "I know this isn't going to do any good; I have my own idea about a special school for my Tina" (Mrs. Tenant). Prior to the initiation of the group there seemed to be a tacit acceptance as the "only way" of what looked like submission on the part of both mother and daughter to each others' controlling behavior, with sudden reversals in who had the initiative, or the upper hand. These reversals would occur in the course of sequences of behavior between mother and daughter which were fragmentary, evanescent, and condensed.

Association of thought in the group occurred on a relatively superficial level. Though the topic of separation of daughter from mother was broached, the underlying issue of abandonment and the feelings involved were not openly discussed. The mothers who were talking seemed unaware in a way that they were associating to the same topic, and this appearance of unawareness itself contributed to the apparent discontinuity of the meeting.

The members of the group superficially discussed a variety of topics: improvement; the meaning of the illness; domination (in the mother-daughter relationship); the superiority of mothers; responsibility for the illness; violence; need for father; separation of daughters from their families.

Acceptance of the doctor's stand that the group be used for the purpose of investigating the situation between mother and daughter, while acceded to intellectually by most of the mothers, was not attended by any action on that score, but by a profound block, and turning to the daughter for her verbalization. When none was forthcoming, or when the words were apparently inappropriate, the mothers showed remarkable and persistent attentiveness to the daughters' deviation, and appeared to be dominating them.

Appearance of Interrelationship—Sessions 4–5

Though the mothers' intellectual acceptance of the group was done together, they at first spoke to the doctor about their daughters' problems individually, as if the others were not present. They then began to speak to one another and about one another, chiefly through expounding or denying the doctor's ideas. There was an early appearance (Session 4) of the Mrs. High-Knowland struggle on domination versus mothering, with the issue as to whether Mrs. High was dominating or mothering Hilda.

In the first meetings there was unverbalized defiance of the doctor by Mrs. High and Mrs. Tenant. Differences in this area did not appear until the fourth session when the Links, in their interaction on the issue of trust and faith in the doctor, brought it out through Laura's open criticism of doctors in general. Their sequence of behavior—of admonition by mother and open defiance by daughter—was the first relationship sequence to come before the group. Mrs. Knowland consistently defended the doctor.

The daughters seemed from the first to be concerned with rejecting the whole venture. They showed apathy and veiled defiance and abandonment of the doctor and mothers. Hilda and Laura by the fourth session joined in supporting one another's defiance of the doctor. Hilda in the seventh session said, "Goodbye, Mother," when Mrs. High showed her dependent feelings. Here the initial, very condensed fragment of their particular sequence of behavior became apparent, and presented the group with the pertinent issue of deviation by daughter.

Discussion in the group was fragmentary and disconnected, attended by deep silences, usually interrupted by Mrs. High with an increasingly querulous and exasperated question of why Hilda persisted in doing what she was doing at the time. Mrs. High in the sixth session compared the doctor to Hilda as not logical. These discussions seemed to flash on and off as the daughters misbehaved in some way. They were attended in time by more pointed divergences about the motives of the mothers in their attentiveness to their children. Mrs. Knowland committed herself through citation of some medical authority or appeal to the doctor for his opinion on "momism." In their interchanges the attitudes of control and superiority, of "mother knows best, do as mother tells you," were challenged at first by the doctor and then by the mothers themselves. As they diverged in their discussions, Mrs. High and Mrs. Knowland seemed to draw closer together in a socially friendly manner.

Appearance of Mothers' Feelings About Focal Issues—Sessions 5–16

In the fifth session, Hilda turned from Mrs. High, after being compliant, and Mrs. High attacked Hilda's obtuseness and lack of ambition. Mrs. Knowland defended Hilda.

After the mothers committed themselves to differences about their daughters' behavior, relationships in other areas appeared. More open rivalry between Mrs. High and Mrs. Knowland for the doctor and the daughters' attention and approval came to view in Session 7. Karen engagingly attacked Mrs. High as a devil. The discussions were more pertinent, carried on longer, but fragmentation occurred quite easily as manifested by the daughters' behavioral aberrations. The mothers still showed marked unawareness of the meaning of their own daughters' statements and feelings.

The daughters for the most part did not express their feelings, but acted out defiance or noncompliance, and with statements such as, "I don't want to work" (Hilda), and in the context of discussion of compliance its designation as "potty" (Karen). Laura expressed resentment at being in the hospital, and this presaged open expression of feelings by the other daughters on the issue of responsibility for the hospitalization.

During this phase the mothers' feelings of despair appeared. First clearly expressed in Session 10, by several mothers as a sense of futility, Mrs. High in Session 17 came out with open despair, when her usual defenses of control, superiority, and "mothering" were rendered ineffective in the group by lack of support of the vocal members, and support was given to expression of feelings.

The mothers' attention was thereby drawn from the daughters to themselves. There was voicing of feelings of anger and vindictiveness toward daughter. This was done chiefly by Mrs. High, who found herself somewhat isolated from the group members when she attacked Hilda. Several of the mothers sympathized with Hilda. In addition, the daughters seemed to draw together as a group, and there seemed to be two groups facing each other.

Appearance of Expression of Daughters' Feelings About Focal Issues—Sessions 17–32

As the mothers' feelings became more evident, the doctor called attention to them. The daughters acted out their rejection of mother's gifts and also some clear independence strivings. They began later to tell of their resentment and spitefulness. Mrs. High and Hilda exhibited a discernible sequence of behavior: estranged dependency; deviation of daughter, acted out or verbalized in terms of abandonment of mother; despair and anger of mother; threats by mother of abandonment of the daughter; decreasing support of the rejecting mother; and increasing support of daughter by the group. Daughter (Hilda) would at this point at times simultaneously attack and come to the rescue of mother with statements like "Let's go, Mother."

Laura and Mrs. Link, in Session 18, went through a sequence of behavior which involved expression of feelings of both relative to the demands each placed on the other. In Session 19, the mothers introduced the question of the unique position they held in relation to their daughters, where the daughters acted as if they missed and were interested chiefly in them, but largely rejected them at visiting time.

Appearance of Acceptance by Mothers of Their Own Problems as Individuals—Sessions 32–50

The mothers agreed on their "brave fronts and otherwise insides" (Mrs. Roper, Session 35). Mrs. High spoke of her own tantrums and sense of martyrdom, and hinted at thoughts of the death of her husband.

The doctor would point out the similarity of the ways of mother to daughter in the area that mother criticized. This would be done chiefly with Mrs. High and at the point of helplessness expressed by her in the face of the rejecting daughter and group. The mother showed remorse and self-recrimination, but in several sessions showed acceptance of the doctor's and the group's words by using them in relation to herself and another mother.

The daughters by the fortieth session became free enough to express their preoccupations, and came out with their feelings of despair and open anger, pertinent to events in the group. The mothers countered with their resentment on exclusion from daughters' world. The daughters attacked specific qualities of their mothers' characters, such as rejectiveness, overprotectiveness and domineering. The mothers critically, yet acceptingly, commented on each others' mothering. Their interchanges with daughter became more violent, when their feelings of hostility and of hopelessness about receiving love from one another came out. Daughter was recognized as a sensitive, unconventional person, quite like mother in her youth. Mother began showing what appeared to be empathy for daughter's suffering and dependent needs.

Appearance of Group-Centered Discussions and of Full Cyclic Sequences in Mother-Daughter Relationship—Session 52

The struggle with the doctor became less intense, and the group discussions became centered on the problems in relationship brought up by its members. The relationship with the daughter was talked about more consistently by Session 52, and returned to spontaneously when the group strayed, as a common problem.

The mothers, showing greater empathy for their daughters' feelings, were responded to, and there were brief episodes of open reconciliation between mother and daughter. This was evidenced most dramatically by the Highs in Session 52.

The mothers spoke of their sense of abandonment by the child, and in Session 58 came to the concept of this as the child they had always felt differently about. They talked of their own experiences and feelings, going through intense emotional experiences with their daughters, of abandonment-recrimination-reconciliation (in Sessions 58 and 61). The discussions carried into areas of anxiety in the mothers and the daughters relative to abandonment of each other, with open display of hostility and death wishes. The group was well on its way toward analysis of its relationships.

3. THE GROUP DYNAMISM

We will now attempt systematically to go over the material presented so far from the point of view of the dynamics of the group. This psychological entity, the group, was related to other groups as entities. Only the barest outlines of this aspect of the group dynamism will be presented, chiefly because of the insufficient data in some areas, and lack of time adequately to process a great deal of data derived from the ward therapy group which the patients attended throughout this experiment.

Social Context of the Group

This group was interdependent with three social units: the community, hospital, and family. The larger community was in the picture through its agencies, the courts, police, hospitals, and neighborhood groups. The hospital community, St. Elizabeths Hospital, was related to this group through its administrative, custodial, recreational, and rehabilitative agencies. This family entered through the larger family groupings, and the immediate household family group.

The mother-daughter group showed its dependence on this social context through representative members, who by character and situation identified with and were able to express those needs and reactions. As a group the mothers and daughters identified with the other groups as objects fulfilling or denying their needs and reactions. These representatives in their behavior indicated a bipartite process—that of representation of their dependent status as regards other groups, and as identifying with these groups. In the group itself, it was often noticeable that the speaker for the needs of the group was at the same time an unacknowledged supervisory authority in the group relative to those needs in the group situation.

This interdependence of groups was manifested by and maintained through certain processes of communication and relationship. Both the social groups and mother-daughter group had their representatives, or spokesmen, the former duly constituted, and the latter arising in accordance with the dominant attitudes and needs of the group in its current situation and their own character traits and immediate personal and social situation. Communication proceeded through formal and informal channels. In both of these channels there was a gradient of personal responsibility, of the extent and nature of responsible verbal commitment. As examples may be cited official and gossip channels of communication, responsible and schizophrenically veiled language. Attention to modes and avenues of communication was of great importance in following the ego growth of the group and its members.

There was little scientifically gathered information on the dynamics of this group prior to the therapeutic intervention. That it did exist as a group was certain. During inclement weather the mothers gathered as a group in the visiting room and when the daughters emerged from behind the locked doors as a group, this meaningful social unit was formed for an hour, then broke up. The mothers then walked as a scattered group to the bus, gathered, and waited there, returning to their respective neighborhoods and family groups. Some stayed to talk to a social worker, the chief of service, clinical director, or even the superintendent of the hospital.

It may be inferred from its functioning after therapy was started that the mothers identified themselves with this group through deep personal motives, involving the mother-child relationship. Of all the relatives of the patients on this chronic ward, *they* chose to visit regularly over the years. Also, the mothers seemed to have set themselves apart from what was estimated to be the preponderant family and neighborhood attitudes toward abandonment of a relatively fruitless relationship.

The mothers identified the community, family, and neighborhood groups as antagonistic groups; witness their statements: "They don't understand." "They want me to stop seeing my daughter." "The hospital doesn't care." "The police took her away."

In effect, these mothers, deeply identified together in their isolation, were sticking it through independent of their home groups, and were utterly dependent on the hospital groups. As such, they had deeply ambivalent attitudes toward the representatives of both of those groups. The spokesmen for the family or neighbors took it upon themselves to express what to them were the dominant attitudes of the group. In this instance the attitudes were regarding the meaning to the individual and social group of the experience of psychosis. These representatives were through their social commitment influential with their groups and evoked in the mothers even more isolative and dependent attitudes.

In the mothers' group itself, the mothers' isolated, "going-it-alone," "it's-my-job-to-cure-her" state and its correlate attitude of utter dependence on the doctor for what to do found its most representative expression in Mrs. High.

Before onset of treatment the mothers' group had only the most rudimentary expression of its attitudes as a group. Though the members were deeply identified with one another, this was on an implicit, or at best a gossip level of responsibility. It appeared that they were fighting off considering themselves, when they thought responsibly, as dependent, isolated, pathetic characters. This disavowed image of self, central to the relationship, was communicated about on a gripe session, gossip level, disavowed in other social contexts, or worn there as a badge of masochistic deviation.

The usual processes in the group centering around problems in dependency and the usages on regulation and control of rivalry and alliance were not in view. In fact, as in groups of psychotics, these processes were best detected through indications of denial of those selfsame processes, an inverse kind of manifestation. The group members did not at the outset of the study identify themselves in any responsible way with the history of their experience together, nor with any traditions, mores, or codes of behavior. Responsible identification occurred later in the group experience, and was focal to the therapeutic movement of the group and its members.

In sum, the mother-daughter group may be described as an aggregate of isolate individuals with strong but generally latent or dissociated bonds of identification, inversely manifest interpersonal group processes, weak internal representative organization (fragmented and latent role taking), communicative processes of stereotyped communication on a responsible level, and gossip, gripe-session type of communication of dependent aspects of relationship. Relationship between group members may be restated to be an identification, largely unspoken, by the mothers with one another as fellow sufferers, coupled with nonresponsible communication with one another of their dependent feelings. Propinquity and association were forced on them and their daughters by physical exigencies and administrative fiat. The daughters were isolated from one another with, as with their mothers, extremely stereotyped, yet markedly individualistic behavior. The mother-daughter pairs showed an extremely closely knit relationship, with coupled dependence-rejection of each other.

Initially, the group members related to the doctor in what they took to be his two capacities—as an administrator and therapist. Actually, he was there as therapist only. The mothers were the vocal ones at first. In keeping with their accustomed ways as visitors the mothers displayed a range of supervisory, dependent attitudes toward the doctor indicative of their extremely subordinate status, while simultaneously displaying superior controlling attitudes toward their daughters. The daughters exhibited schizophrenic defiance and compliance toward the doctor and their mothers. Both mothers and daughters appeared to insist that the capacities of therapist and administrator were identical, that the therapist should act authoritatively and decisively. Therapy began when the doctor took steps to clarify that point.

As an administrative representative of the hospital the doctor was expected by the mothers to reassure, order, forbid, and decide points at issue. The role of the therapist—namely, that of guidance of the patient in investigation, elucidation, and education in the field of interpersonal relationship—was a new one to the experience of this group.

From the limited observation of this group before therapy began and inferences from later material it was fairly evident that the members were involved in issues relative to two main aspects of the same experience, the experience of visiting-visited and mothering-mothered. They were involved as members of the hospital community and as mother-daughter pairs. How the hospital regulated the act of visiting and took care of the mothers and daughters were issues involved in this experience and brought in the dependence on both the hospital community and its representatives. Issues involving power struggles with the hospital in this regard were the treatment, psychologic and physical of the patients; the small, common waiting room; policies regarding privileges and clothing of patients and of food gifts (candy, cakes) before mealtime.

In representing their positions in these regards to the hospital authorities the mothers maintained chiefly underground modes of relationship and communication, marked by covert defiance, despairing compliance, and occasional isolated rebellion. Ostensibly there existed a code of behavior in the visiting room: visitors attended to their own business, acted sociably, and in a socially distant manner exchanged historical data and views on the illness of daughter and vied for privileges.

The struggles of the group members around the issues involved in the act of mothering-mothered were more immediate and overt. In taking positions on those issues the members displayed aspects of their personalities markedly different from those involved in the social act of visiting. Mothers, for instance, at times smiled as visitors and frowned as mothers.

Initiation of therapy involved resolution of personal issues for the psychiatrist. In response to the request for medical intervention in their situation by the mothers, the doctor had to decide in which ego capacity as therapist he would intervene—as a sort of administrator, role-playing manipulator, or analytic therapist, or a mixture of the three. This decision was quickly made, but involved estimation of his capacity for closer personal contact with extremely dependent yet resistive individuals, in an experience of a trying and frustrating nature. This process coincided with the perception of the group's accessibility to therapeutic intervention, on the basis of past and anticipated experience. The doctor anticipated the impact on himself and the group of relinquishment of administrative type of controls, with the problems in acceptance of his new capacity as a guide of the group and individuals on the evolution of more responsible participation in the experience.

With the internal decision came external action toward structuring a situation most appropriate for systematic therapeutic work. This involved the exploration of dependent aspects of relationships and evolution of new, more appropriate approaches to the group's and individual's control of self and environment.

In sum, the initial therapeutic situation involved an inherent shifting of capacities and relationships for all the participants toward greater personal responsibility. The therapist thwarted the participants' control mechanism through his emotional committal and also through abstinence from gratification of the group members' expectation of his adherence to their established social control mechanisms. This nonadherence brought out the dependencies of all the participants and rendered their exploration and working through imperative.

The mothers and daughters were "on their own feet," supported and guided by the doctor, in an effort to investigate their relationships.

The group manifested this new state of affairs as a group with behavior and communication indicative of an open power struggle about the issue of dependency on one another. In their representation on this score the mothers from the first identified the doctor, the daughters, and society as the agents who should enable them to be happy and peaceful. The daughters and, in part of his emotional involvement, the doctor resisted this demand, responding with hostility and aversion.

This group issue was the chief one in the first four sessions, and in its partial resolution there was evolved the therapeutic capacity of the group. On this issue the group members appeared to act as responsible individuals but in reality either speaking through others, or denying relationships to others. There was an intensely rivalrous underground struggle with other group members about control of the group and assumption of separate identities and self-determined emotional commitment, as opposed to the dependently acted-out commitment through others.

The roles the members took on this issue of control and dependency were the characteristic ones found in all groups in response to an actual problem. This refers to the social group roles of politician, teacher, philosopher, audience, clown, antisocial deviant, etc. In addition, the members operated in capacities relative to representation of the personal problems under scrutiny: the dominating mother, openly dependent mother, therapist's good little girl, mother's bad boy or girl, mother's little baby, etc.

These roles and capacities were centered largely about

the therapist at first. The action took place on group, three-group, two-group, and individual levels, and on unconscious and conscious levels in each of those. The first member to represent the group was Mrs. High who spoke for and represented her daughter's resistance to the doctor (and herself). This was followed by representation on the part of the other mothers of their daughters' problems in resistance. Thus a range of commitment to the doctor was displayed, running from Mrs. High's appeasing-provocative dependence, Mrs. Link's protestation of faith, Mrs. Tenant's egocentric denial of hope, and Mrs. Knowland's self-effacing acceptance of the doctor's word as an authority. The dynamic tensions between the mothers and within the mothers were still underground, manifest only indirectly in the differences in their initial approach to the doctor.

The daughters' subgroup displayed their acted-out negation of relationship, except for Laura, who in a three-group relationship with mother and the doctor, openly committed herself to an identity as a disbeliever, rejecting the doctor, and thereby broaching on an ego level the issue of meaningfully verbalized abandonment.

This commitment on Laura's part presaged the acceptance by the group of the therapeutic usage of expression by the individual of her own dependent problems on the basis of her own personal identity. Interrelationships about and including dependent aspects of the personality of the members had appeared. In addition, a nuclear fragmentary representation of what was later to become a definite, responsible engagement took place in the appearance of a familial couple communicating significantly about issues between them. The group was moving away from the visiting-room stereotype.

This surprising commitment of an open disavowal and abandonment of the doctor evoked further movement in the group. This was manifested first by the politician member,

Mrs. High, with expression of her own underlying feelings of disappointment in her mothering role with Hilda, an advance from her self-righteous badgering of daughter. This movement proceeded through the range of ego defenses present in the mothers, with each, in reference to her daughter, speaking either directly of her feelings (as Mrs. Tenant), or referring to those of another (Mrs. Knowland about Mrs. High). This took the form of indirectly rivalrous expression about issues, in this case that of the relationship to the doctor as a therapist, and the problem of control in the mother-daughter relationship, as presented by Mrs. High. Alliances and disalliances were formed in the maintenance and relinquishment of outer and inner controls.

As noted earlier, the first to rebel against control of both the mother and the doctor was Laura, who in this act accepted the doctor's request for emotional participation in accordance with the dependent identity of the members. Mrs. Knowland identified herself, in her controlled way, with Laura and the doctor in upholding this stand, thereby identifying herself with the dependent, rebellious group. Mrs. High moved from her initially appeasing role to exposition of more open defiance.

The relationships of the group on the other levels mentioned—the community and hospital—went into abeyance during the sessions as the members met the interpersonal challenge of the moment in the group. However, there was evidence that members communicated with the chief of service, representing the views of the group on their problems as visitors and mothers.

The appearance of the mothers' dependent feelings about focal issues followed the failure of Mrs. High's controlling ways with her daughter. This failure followed the doctor's abstinence from social support of her efforts and his, Laura's and Mrs. Knowland's ego commitment to the side of the dependent other, in this case, Hilda. Differences between Mrs. Knowland and Mrs. High on Mrs. High's relationship to Hilda and the doctor marked the appearance of open conflict in the mothers' subgroup, marked by rivalry in mode of approach to and for possession of the doctor and the daughter.

This representation in the group of the mothers' feelings, supervisory and dependent, brought into communication and therefore reality testing the various aspects of the personality functioning—ego and certain aspects of the superego—of the mothers. At the same time, their identity as mothers, as members of the mothers' subgroup, was established. They related here as a group and as individuals to their actual daughters instead of through the doctor as formerly. They still utilized the doctor to start off relationships in this area, but soon, as a group, turned to the mother-daughter relationship.

During this development the daughters were active, resisting the advances of their mothers and the doctor. In the range of expression on this point, Laura made the first committed statement of resentment at specific treatment by her mother.

With Laura as leader the daughters rejected the previously eagerly awaited food gifts of their mothers and in a semipolitical, histrionic way evidenced strivings toward independence. With this expression of identity as a group, the daughters as individuals made movement in their relationships with their mothers, and identifiable interactional sequences between mother-daughter pairs appeared, a development of great importance, opening the avenue to analysis of the individual.

As the mothers openly identified with one another as mothers, the correlate process of identifying the daughter in one another became clearer. They formed identifiable mother-daughter pairs of their own. Their supervision of each others' behavior in regard to the daughter and doctor

became less distant, obscure, and dependent, and more pertinent. They began to assume more helpful capacities. Extra-
group contacts became quite prominent, with an alternation
of "mothering" one another and exhibition of dependent
needs, and alliance against authoritarian members of the family groups, especially husband.

The leaders in the group—Mrs. High and Mrs. Knowland—continued as such, with the former still assuming her
capacity of expressing the supervisory as well as dependent
aspects of relationship of the group members as the group
made movement. The others, especially Mrs. Angell, participated increasingly in more overt, personal form, reflecting increased security in the social unit. Defenses were dropped,
and the feelings behind them appeared. This phenomenon
appeared as a confluent affair, with the mothers agreeing on
their feelings of futility, despair and anger at nonrealization
of the idealized image invested in this particular child. Following this manifestation, the mothers arrived at the concep-
tion of the daughter in the image of the mother when she was
a child.

Thereupon the group moved toward an elucidation of
the feelings of mother and daughter, with increased personal
responsibility for their own feelings, their own inadequacies,
and the part they had played in the genesis of the present situation. This was accompanied by increased acceptance of
their dependence on the doctor. The group had attained for
itself an identity as a therapeutic group.

4. The Relationship Sequences of the Mother-Daughter Pairs

General

The course of the group revolved about the therapeutic
problem of the relationship of mother and daughter. This relationship at the inception of the group seemed to manifest

itself as a struggle about conformity to or deviation from the defenses of the mother. The mother seemed to depend on the spontaneity and initiative taken by the daughter in this regard. In this struggle the mother dependently exercised control of the situation. In the group, she covertly insisted that it was *her* job to get the daughter well, while submissively asking the doctor for guidance. This submission was attended by a singular lack of awareness of the significance of the doctor's communications, except as something to be blindly repeated, ignored, and later defied. The daughters, on the other hand, were compliant to the extent of sitting there, and in the case of Laura, clearly defiant.

Study of the changes in this relationship as they unfolded revealed, for the various mother-daughter pairs, specific sequences of behavior which gradually became clearer to the extent that they could be anticipated. Present in obscure, condensed, and latent form in the earliest communication between the mother and daughter, this sequence became clearer, less fragmentary, and more manifest as the cycle was repeatedly passed through.

On further study, we find that the behavior patterns of the mothers and their daughters to each other appeared in the following sequence:

(1) The point of departure in the sequence usually was a communication to the daughter, ranging from what "she ought to do" in the case of Mrs. High, to a direct physical "caring for" maneuver on the part of Mrs. Tenant. Both mothers would look to the doctor for his response, and show little awareness of their impact on the other group members. The daughter had the initiative, which she took by deviating from the mother's wish.

(2) When a daughter deviated, her mother's attentiveness was focused on the deviation, and efforts at control followed. In the case of the Highs, daughter was admonished.

Tina was pulled down to mother's lap. At this point, the daughter at first displayed complete apathy or apathetic conformity. After very few sessions, the daughters, after defying the doctor, as a means of deviating from mother's compliance to him, defied their mothers openly.

(3) With mother's control of the situation threatened, her daughter was subjected to intensified efforts at control. As her control failed, mother displayed at first despair, then anger.

(4) Another mother or daughter defended the daughter who had been attacked. This was accompanied by implicit attack and then open rejection of the originally controlling mother. She was at first supported by mothers with similar defenses, and sides were taken about the mother and the daughter in question. This occurred openly or implicitly with each mother. Mrs. High was early in the group's course attacked by Mrs. Knowland over her domination of Hilda. Mrs. Tenant defended her, sides were taken, but there was gradual relinquishment of support, and eventual isolation of Mrs. High on the question of her attacks on Hilda. Later, Mrs. High attacked Mrs. Tenant in regard to her babying of Tina. Still later, Mrs. Angell was attacked by Mrs. High and Mrs. Knowland for overprotectiveness toward Astrid.

Rivalry for the doctor played a part in accentuating the attack on the mother and bringing it out into the open. In time the daughter defended herself through counterattack.

(5) When the mothers were despairing and angry and somewhat isolated and attacked by the others, remorse, and some awareness of the feelings of the daughter as someone who is attacked were shown in varying degrees. An increasing receptivity to critical information about herself appeared, with communication to her by the doctor and the group members of the similarities between her own and her daughter's preoccupations and ways.

(6) Then sympathetic communication to the mother by her own or another daughter, and direct communication of the need for affection by the daughter to the mother appeared.

(7) This was followed by recrimination between mother and daughter over past rejection of daughter by mother, with attempts to appease daughter alternating with mutual despair and abandonment of each other.

(8) There then was reversion to the former state of daughter's vengeful isolation and mother's righteous and superioristic defenses.

As they repeated the sequence of estranged dependency, deviation, despair and anger, abandonment, remorse, reconciliation, recrimination, and again estrangement, they became more aware of their vengeful hostility, dependency and loneliness, and their vulnerability to their daughters' manipulations. The similarity of their preoccupations to their daughters' became more apparent to them. The daughters gradually lowered their defenses against show of feeling, became less bitter, demanding, and retaliative, and showed more initiative in reaching out to their mothers.

Some husbands and grandmothers were mentioned in this sequence when the mothers experienced despair and anger, chiefly in a display of their bitter feelings toward their husbands for their weakness or authoritarianism, and toward grandmothers for their possessiveness.

Changes in Relationships

The Highs

The relationship of this pair changed considerably by the end of the observation. It moved from the obscure estranged equilibrium of the outset through numerous cycles or sequences of behavior to a considerably more open relationship.

These sequences closely approximated the one described earlier. They seemed to take off from the point where mother, requesting compliance by Hilda, seemed to be in control of the situation.

Hilda deviated in the early sessions through her rattling of paper, with mother calling attention to it. The encounter was brief, and the doctor's request for examination of the meaning of the action resulted in group action of display of defensive attitudes by the mothers. There was no observable interaction between this mother and daughter, but a clear one between the Links about faith in the doctor.

In the fourth session, however, Hilda, apparently following Laura's lead of earlier sessions, called to her mother, "Goodbye, Mother," and left, when Mrs. High complained to the doctor that she had expressed her feelings without return in kind from her daughter. Mrs. High then intensified her attentiveness to her daughter's behavior. It may be conjectured that the openness of Hilda's rebellious rejection of mother stemmed partly from the open rejection involved when mother turned from daughter to doctor.

In the fifth session, this sequence of behavior was repeated, centering on Hilda's lack of ambition and need for correction. Hilda defied her mother by asking for a return to the ward. Mrs. High was on the verge of tears, and the other patients laughed at her. This action by the daughters' subgroup apparently led to commitment by the mothers. Mrs. Knowland defended Hilda as self-assertive and as having a sense of futility. Mrs. Tenant defended Mrs. High. Mrs. High despairingly asked Hilda to embarrass her by saying something that she had done to Hilda—to accuse her of putting her in school to get rid of her.

This expectation and request for punishment marked

movement in the behavioral sequence toward appearance of Mrs. High's own dependent needs. The participation of the group members in the interaction was of note. The daughters rejected and sneered at the one who showed dependent feelings, Mrs. High.

In the eighth session, she attacked Hilda and the doctor more intensely and openly. She was rejected by Mrs. Knowland and laughed at repeatedly by Karen, both Knowlands participating in the Highs' problem of the dependent demand. Mrs. High experienced despair and anger and a growing sense of isolation from the group as she repeatedly insisted that Hilda (also apparently meaning herself) was oblivious to what was going on, and that she "had to break the pattern." Hilda cried, "I don't want to work," apparently expressing a feeling of both mother and daughter.

Hilda repeatedly and more openly rejected Mrs. High's advances. She schizophrenically tested mother's awareness of her needs by questions such as what Mrs. High would do for her cold if she came home. Mrs. High's answer was appropriate to the treatment of a physical ailment rather than daughter's emotional cold.

Mrs. High intensified her display of despair and anger in many fragmentary interactions with Hilda in Sessions 10 through 26. Hilda increasingly acted out in clearer form her defiance, joining with Laura.

Hilda, in Session 27, began showing her feelings of despair, anger, and loneliness. Mrs. High, in an exchange with Mrs. Tenant in which they identified with one another in their dependent feelings, replied that "life was a burden" without Hilda. She mentioned her hopelessness about Hilda's "building a romance about another person," and wanted to "shake up" Hilda when she misbehaved.

The relationship sequence moved still another step when Mrs. High began showing receptivity to information from the group on herself in Session 35. She also mentioned acceptance of Hilda's behavior, although this acceptance was "hollow."

In this session there was also movement in the mother-daughter relationship sequence, when Hilda, intolerant of the emotional situation, pulled Rae's hair when she cried. Mrs. High "cracked down" on Hilda. Hilda told the doctor that her mother was the cause of her destructiveness, but reached out to her mother for reconciliation by apologizing for pulling Rae's hair.

In Session 48, Mrs. High turned on Mrs. Tenant for her babying of Tina, reflecting the hostility she had incurred in identifying with deviant "baby Hilda." She also was showing efforts at differentiating herself from Hilda, and on her own rejecting her as a baby.

By Session 49, Mrs. High was talking of her own need to change, and Hilda attempted to please her. This apparently set the stage for a sequence between them on Hilda's anger and despair, in which Hilda tore her dress and mother accepted it as emotionally motivated, and attempted to accept the emotions involved.

In succeeding sessions, Hilda came out more openly with her own feelings of despair, anger and loneliness. Mrs. High would alternately disparage and accept Hilda's feelings. Hilda stated in Session 55, "I want to get my life going right now," and also spoke of "coffins and death." In Session 57 she was bitter and recriminative on her hospitalization. In Session 58, she burst into tears, with "I don't want death, Mother." In Session 59, Mrs. High, at first negative, accepted Hilda's "life on an ocean wave," as applicable to Hilda's current existence.

In Session 63, Mrs. High, dealing with her own individual problems, exhibited her pride in her ability to stand up to her husband's rejection and ridicule relative to Mrs. High's continued interest in Hilda. This interest now was in another person, whom Mrs. High in a limited way could differentiate herself from, and reject on her own. This separation of the daughter's identity from her own was of focal importance in the development of their relationship.

In Session 67, Mrs. High and Hilda went through a sequence of rejection of Hilda, followed by Hilda's tearing her dress, and then a tracing down, with the group's participation, of why Hilda had torn her dress, to Hilda's being "heartbroken when mother doesn't come."

Hilda's social behavior in the group improved considerably after this. She was fairly successful as hostess at her birthday party. In Session 71, she asked for help with her problem, "Carry me, I can't walk." She came out with her preoccupations on death and menstruation.

Mrs. High in succeeding sessions joined with the mothers in the group on their problems in needing to change. In Session 77, she attacked Hilda again on the lack of hope in her letters, but in succeeding sessions showed increasing awareness of her own problems in pressing the attacks. She stated, "Hilda is doing to me what I do to Mr. High."

Mr. High's death at this point brought little overt change in the relationship between Hilda and her mother. Mrs. High joined with the mothers in attacking the hospital for not listening to them (similar to previous attacks on their husbands). The mothers, including Mrs. High, guiltily remarked on their husbands as concealing their crying and as being seriously preoccupied with daughter's welfare. Mrs. High, in Session 82, was contrite over her nagging of Hilda (as she had Mr. High), "Can't stop it, though I try."

In Session 88, Mrs. High told of her understanding of Hilda's deviant ways through her own reversion to biting her nails and eating all day in her recent period of mourning. Hilda told Mrs. Tenant of the good qualities of a private school which she had attended. Mrs. Tenant had been repeatedly referring to the school as what Tina needed (implying that she, or rather her husband, had failed Tina in not having the money to send her to the special school, rather than failing her emotionally).

In Session 92, Mrs. High spoke for Hilda on Hilda's displeasure at her own mannerisms, and of her hope of changing them. Hilda's defiance of mother, and mother's despair and abandonment of daughter took less extreme forms and both seemed more hopeful.

Hilda's social behavior continued improving. She took part in occupational therapy and psychodrama. She appeared to be more contemplative and less distractable in the ward therapeutic group, and brought up questions relative to the events in the mothers' group. She spoke hopefully of going home.

This pair had worked through the problem of control to the extent that in the group situation they were able to communicate relatively freely. They had communicated in a clear manner on many of the issues present between them. Mother had gone through and faced some of her feelings incident to loss of control of the situation between daughter and self. Despair and anger had been experienced in the context of a situation of abandonment by daughter and the group. Her flight from anxiety in the immediate interpersonal relationship to attentiveness to someone else's feelings—daughter, husband, group member, or society—had been to some extent checked and reversed. Her dependence on Hilda was consequently lessened. Daughter's emotional and realistic dependence on mother became more manifest.

Daughter in the cycles experienced a breaking down of her defenses against show of feelings. Her loneliness, bitterness, and anger appeared. Reconciliation with mother afterwards was each time on a more realistic level.

Mother, and to some extent daughter, gave evidence of

identifying the other as a separate person, or having rights and feelings of her own. This separation of identities seemed to have occurred secondary to, or coincident with, the experience of abandonment of one another during their relationship cycles within the therapeutic context. Having experienced and survived the dependent state involved, they were able to identify those feelings in themselves, rather than through the other person, as was formerly quite clear in the case of Mrs. High.

The maneuvers of both in nagging one another, calling on the other to abandon them first became apparent in the group. This awareness was expressed in remarks like Mrs. High's, "Hilda does to me what I do to Mr. High."

The Knowlands

The participation of this pair was from the first through other members of the group, with little or no direct communication between one another. This was done early in the group through the struggle between Mrs. High and Hilda.

Whereas Mrs. High challenged the doctor, Mrs. Knowland asked him for advice on what to read, and offered him complementary statements by other psychiatrists, many of them attacking the other mothers, especially Mrs. High. While Mrs. Knowland paid attention to the doctor, she kept Karen's masturbation under surveillance out of the corner of her eye.

The Knowlands in large part identified themselves in the group through the struggles of the Highs, as noted earlier. Mrs. Knowland attacked Mrs. High as too domineering and identified with Hilda. Karen, for her part, continued with her deviations, and also attacked Mrs. High as a devil. When the other members told of their despair, and deep discouragement, Mrs. Knowland asserted her optimism, "Instead of mourning, I'm beaming." However, when the other members of the group came to open display of their anger, she revealed that she feared her daughter's anger.

There was very little verbalized evidence of change in the relationship of Karen and Mrs. Knowland during the group sessions. There was a marked decrease in masturbation and dress chewing on Karen's part. She decreased her mocking laughter and veiled attacks on Mrs. High. By the fifty-second session, this was no longer present.

At the same time, Mrs. Knowland showed more tolerance for her daughter's deviation in the group, but with very little verbalization about it. Her attacks on Mrs. High became more pointed, and she led the other mothers to discussion of what was wrong with themselves. Her own fear of Karen's anger came up, but was broached in her usual affectless way. She never came to open commitment of her own dependent self, or deviated from her identification with the doctor as a benevolent authority.

Karen improved symptomatically, with longer visits home, increased interest in other members of her family, especially her father, whom she went out of her way to please. She dressed better, lost weight, and appeared to be making a social recovery.

Of the daughters, Karen seemed to have made the most social progress, though her emotional participation was at best obscure. Much of this progress was reflected in the easing of the obscure tension over masturbation and dress chewing on Karen's part. The mother and daughter also seemed to use the group's social process as a platform for other socializing enterprises, such as going to movies, concerts, etc., where mother reported back to the group the success of the venture, apparently deriving a sort of competitive security in being way ahead outside the group activity.

The Tenants

Mrs. Tenant usually spoke about and for Tina while caressing or holding on to her. Her words were to the effect that there was no hope for Tina in this institution. She would add that Tina could not understand what was happening, and that she was so different. Tina would at this point laugh mockingly at the doctor and other members of the group.

In the fourth session, at the point where tension mounted when Hilda and Laura defied their mothers, Mrs. Tenant and Tina embraced, and Mrs. Tenant looked defiantly at the doctor. When the group discussed the anger of the patients in the eighteenth session, Mrs. Tenant emphasized her feeling that it "means everything to keep Tina satisfied." In the twenty-third session she expressed feeling for her daughter's suffering. In the next session she spoke of how she had always regarded Tina as a two- to three-year-old.

In Session 29, she joined with Mrs. Link in telling of the desperate priority daughter played over her own needs. Mrs. Tenant disclaimed shame for this child, and felt that the others were saying that she was an unfeeling woman, and that this was the cause of Tina's illness.

She wondered with the others, in Session 35, why the daughters treated them like children and were dominating, and voiced feelings relevant to why they "deserved such treatment," as "some terrible thing it must have been. . . ."

In Session 36, Mrs. Tenant, in asking about Tina's relation to other patients on the ward, took the blame for Tina's dependence on people. In Session 48, Mrs. High attacked Mrs. Tenant for her babying of Tina, told her to let go of her hand and see what would happen. Mrs. Tenant showed dismay and, in the ensuing meetings, supported Mrs. High less, but gradually relinquished physical contact with Tina. Tina for her part began to insist on sitting up when mother started to drag her to her lap.

In Session 61, Mrs. Tenant reported Tina's increasing powers of communication, and Tina's mocking laugh came under discussion. Miss Sheppard paid attention in the sessions to when Tina laughed, and remarked on its appropriateness. Simultaneously, there was a marked decrease in the laughter, which at times in the past had made group discussion almost impossible.

In Session 87, Mrs. Tenant came out with her guilt at not sending Tina to a private school. In Session 94, she complained of Tina's attachment to an attendant, a complaint voiced by Mrs. Roper previously. Tina showed increasing display of emotion on the ward, and a proclivity for physically close relationships with the more intellectual patients. During altercations between patients in the group sessions, she showed participation through attack on the losing member.

This pair had gone through an extremely slow separation from one another, through participation with the other group members on the issues pertinent to the mother-infant relationship. They seemed to be fixated in problems of relinquishment of physical propinquity and attentiveness and understanding of anything outside the immediate mother-infant relationship. Mother's anguish at separation from daughter was to some extent broached, and movement was made from her defensive denial of Tina's and her own awareness of anything outside their relationship. Mrs. Tenant had become reoriented toward their problem; Tina appeared to have moved from her complete compliance to a passively defiant mode of behavior.

The Links

This pair showed the most open relationship from the first. The issue of patience and trust in the doctor was broached in the first session, as an urging of Laura by Mrs. Link. By the fourth session, Laura was openly and with affect defiant of the doctor and his purposes, to the distress of her mother.

Mrs. Link joined with Mrs. Tenant and Mrs. High in describing, in the tenth session, her despair in missing her daughter. Laura turned on her in a disconnected accusation, "Why did you take me in the bedroom?" apparently referring to mother's bedding with daughter instead of her husband, since daughter's infancy. Mother became quite defensive, but the interaction did not proceed further at this point.

In the sixteenth session, Laura joined with Hilda in defying the mothers by spilling candy on the floor. Laura declared, "The name was Thomas Jefferson (Declaration of Independence). . . . I already told you. I blasted you out." She also stated that Tina was unable to express her feelings (Laura's mode of talking about herself through reference to others). Mrs. Link was abjectly despairing, and wondered if Laura understood her feelings.

In the seventeenth session, Laura petulantly complained of being confined in the hospital. In the eighteenth session, Mrs. Link, after pleading for response from her daughter, piteously cried over Laura's resentment of her, and Laura acted tough, then pleasant, as soon as mother cried. She again pointed, in this sequence, to Tina. She referred this time to Tina's "craziness," a quality she probably meant as pertinent to herself.

In the ensuing sessions, mother and daughter participated in the other mother-daughter interactions, chiefly between the Highs, rather than in direct, open quarrels in the group. In Session 24, Mrs. Link asserted her dependency on Laura's response of satisfaction for her own happiness. In Session 27, Mrs. Link brought out the first of what were to be repeated complaints on Laura's preference for her brothers, later for Mr. Link. Along with these complaints were reports of longer periods home on visit, and of a new-found sociability on Laura's part.

In Session 36, Mrs. Link told at length of Laura's openly expressed desire for affection, and her resentment of her mother. The issue of Laura's bossing her mother was broached as part of a general group discussion, and Laura gaily demonstrated her bossy ways in regard to her mother and the doctor. Laura playfully attacked the doctor.

In Session 57, Laura stated she had blisters in her mouth when the group discussed receiving love from mothers.

Mrs. Link spoke, in Session 74, of her "broken heart," and tearfully told of her desperate feeling that she was cheating on Laura, who liked Mr. Link (apparently for keeping them apart). In Session 88, Laura wept despairingly when her mother asked her for response, then moved closer to her, when Mrs. Link complained of Laura's turning from her to Mr. Link. Laura cried to the doctor that he had given her back her feelings, and was grateful for that, and that now she needed to control them.

In their sequences of behavior, mother and daughter were able, in the group setting, to communicate with one another on many of the issues between them, and on their problems as individuals. Mrs. Link's prudishness and estrangement from her husband, apparently with determinants in her relationship with her own mother, were reflected in her dependent closeness and possessive physical relationship with her daughter. She urged on daughter attitudes of trust and faith about which she herself was deeply ambivalent. Daughter reflected these early in the group, in her cynical statements regarding the doctors.

Mrs. Link was brought face to face with her hostile distance maneuvers in regard to her husband through the person of her daughter. The issue of intimacy with her husband, manifested by Laura in warmth to her father, likewise was broached.

There was a great deal of communication on these issues, with considerable separation of mother from daughter, with, in Laura's words, freeing of her feelings. Both faced some of the panic and despair involved in abandonment of each other. The sequences revolved about affect-laden, non-intellectualized issues of acceptance-rejection. They were to a large extent acted out, and were quite brief. In the process, mother and daughter were either split asunder, or else close and overtly affectionate.

Laura's social improvement continued, with visits home for extended periods.

The Ropers

There was relatively little direct communication between Mrs. Roper and Rae. Most of it was done, as with the Knowlands, through the other group members. The two at first sat close to one another, Rae aloof, Mrs. Roper quite attentive to the doctor and the group members.

In Session 35, Mrs. Roper came out with her "brave fronts and otherwise insides," identifying herself in that regard. Rae cried afterwards (for her mother?). Hilda's attack on Rae at this point may have indicated Rae's going over to the side of the mother and Hilda's reaction formation to tears and softness. Mrs. Roper later in the session, during the discussion by the other mothers of the daughters' overriding natures, noted that in Rae, stating that Rae treated her like a child.

From Session 44 on, Rae showed antagonism toward her mother. Mrs. Roper repeatedly mentioned Rae's friendliness toward her father, and Rae's way of cutting off conversation with her. In Session 47, Mrs. Roper advised Mrs. Springer on the futility of advice per se in arriving at understandings with daughter. Mrs. Roper had been seeking advice exclusively up to then.

Mrs. Roper showed considerable helplessness and some unverbalized anger (her throat would puff up and become red), when Rae would turn from her in an increasingly annoyed manner. In Session 68, Rae told of having no mother and of being upset when her grandmother died. In Session 71, Mrs. Roper reproached herself for failing to bring her daughter up properly.

In Session 85, Mrs. Roper brought out a point of issue with Rae, her smoking, as something she should not have pursued so intently, since it was only a manifestation of Rae's illness. Mrs. Knowland noted that it was more likely that it was a point of conflict with Mr. Roper. Mrs. Roper then told of "going to pieces" after the last session, and of her increasing despair over not having Rae home.

Again, in Session 86, Mrs. Roper complained of Rae's coldness to her, and warmth to Mr. Roper, and of Rae's having the upper hand in regard to discipline. In Session 93, Mrs. Roper stated that activity on the part of the daughter was not helpful until "the pressure is relieved first." In Session 94, she noted Rae's physically expressed attachment to an attendant. This attachment was exhibited by Rae in a provocative and mocking manner, in apparent caricature of the past relationship with mother. Mrs. Roper appeared distressed, with increasing signs of unverbalized anger.

The issues of social and sexual propriety, which had been prominent in this pair's relationship, were communicated to one another indirectly, through the group discussion. Mrs. Roper complained to the group of Rae's going to New York to hear a crooner, and Rae's smoking. Rae would express annoyance nonverbally. There was some provocative (toward mother) display of preference for Mr. Roper and an attendant on Rae's part. Rae began resisting attendance at the group.

In both there was definite "getting back at" Mrs. Roper.

The group served chiefly to reorient Mrs. Roper, and to enable Rae to emancipate herself a little from Mrs. Roper. Mrs. Roper, however, could not reciprocate this behavior. There was increasing display of despair on both their parts, and in Rae, some of her anger, as annoyance.

They apparently failed to separate themselves from one another sufficiently to experience feelings of abandonment, and then to undergo reconciliation.

The Springers

Mrs. Springer, her spinster sister, Miss Sheppard, and Sally began attending the group at about the time when the members had reached the point where they were able to instruct the new members in the approach to the daughter through the understanding of the mother, and of the situation which existed between mother and daughter. Mrs. Springer was steered away from her advocacy of faddist interventions to expression of her feelings and, in Session 51, stated that she was sorry for Sally, but wanted to share the things that were important to her. However, she ignored Sally's expressed feelings of being "dead because of lack of affection," and Sally expressed futility.

In Session 53, Mrs. Springer attacked Sally for her sexually-colored behavior during the watching of a football game, and denied Sally's awareness of the events and of her own feelings. Sally and Hilda made mocking noises. Mrs. High defended Sally, as reacting to something that had been forced on her. Both Sally and Mrs. Springer mentioned violence toward an offender.

In Session 54, Mrs. Springer indicated that most mothers lacked proper mother-care instincts, thereby presenting her own problem. Sally then began furiously attacking her mother. She stated, "You reach out and the black sky falls on you." In Session 67, she brought out, in relation to demands for response on Mrs. Springer's part, "Get off my back, you fucking idiot. You are like living hopeless beings. You're dying."

In Session 85, Mrs. Springer spoke of getting down to the level of the daughters and showing feelings. Sally stated, "It means there's a beginning of spring, doesn't it?"

In Session 91, Mrs. Springer compared herself to Sally in her misery-driven wild destructiveness, with, "If I had been a man I would have been a fighter, not taken anything off of anybody." She and Mrs. Roper agreed that it was necessary to relieve the pressure inside the patients first, that activity (presumably also faddist activity) was of no real help. She spoke of herself as feeling trapped.

In the ninety-fifth session, she spoke of the daughters' feelings of inferiority as due to expectation of failure, and later indirectly wished the hospital would drop into the earth. She stated that the patients were envious of other, happier people, and did not want them to be happy. In this, it may be inferred, she spoke of her own feelings. She spoke in the last session of the daughters' dreams which the mothers could not find out, and agreed with Mrs. Knowland on the mothers' tendency to reach the daughters on only their own terms.

The mother-daughter relationship changed to the extent that they had at the end of the observation begun expressing their intense feelings of dependency and hostility to one another. From a sullen, withdrawn person, Sally began showing outbursts of feeling, at first fragmentary and apparently inappropriate, then in more pertinent and clearer interactions, extremely moving to her mother and the group. Mrs. Springer was undergoing a marked reorientation in her approach to her daughter, and began facing some of her guilt and hostility. The problem of abandonment and reconciliation, noted in the Highs' mother-daughter sequence, was just broached at the end of the observation, but no overt reconciliation between mother and daughter was obtained.

The Angells

Mrs. Angell and Astrid plunged right into the group process, at the point when the group was able to maintain group-centered discussions, and the mother-daughter sequence between the Highs involved intense, open recrimination by daughter to mother, talk of death on daughter's part, and scenes of abandonment-reconciliation between mother and daughter. Mrs. Angell's defenses of repression, looking on the bright side and "understanding" the daughter as being sick carried very little weight with the group members, and were soon largely relinquished for more personally appropriate expression.

In Session 55, Mrs. Angell stated, "It's confusing to me," when Astrid described herself as "a grown-up woman who has turned herself into a child." In Session 57, Astrid was bitter against mother for her complicity in hospitalizing her. Mrs. Angell mentioned her own wishes to daydream. Later in the session, she spoke of Astrid as being grief-stricken, and, therefore, refusing affection.

In Session 58, in reply to mother's question as to what she wanted, Astrid stated that she wanted to commit suicide. Astrid consoled Mrs. High who was distressed over rejection by Hilda, and gave Hilda a (symbolically significant) orange.

Mrs. Angell was attacked as overprotective of Astrid in Session 62, by Mrs. High and Mrs. Knowland. In turn she blamed Astrid's paternal grandmother. Mrs. Knowland blamed Mrs. Angell's dislike of the personality of her first husband, manifested in Astrid, for rejection of Astrid. Astrid in this session attacked her mother as insane, and as having sexual relations with a dog.

In Session 65, Astrid complained of having been given things and then knocked down. In Session 67, she spoke of having been locked in jail and left there. In the next session she joined with Sally on her lack of affection from mother, and stated, "It's a terrible thing to destroy anybody's heart."

Mrs. Angell missed Session 71 because of hospitalization for a "heart attack." In the course of the session, Astrid consoled Mrs. High as kind, when Mrs. High showed distress at Hilda's attacks. When Mrs. Angell had returned in Session 76, and stated she could not help babying her daughter since she was ill, Astrid blurted out, "This is your [and my?] punishment for being so guilty." Mrs. Angell as yet could not separate herself from daughter sufficiently to respond to her abandonment and conscience-provoking attacks appropriately.

In Session 77, in response to mother's expectation for response from her, Astrid stated, "I don't care what you say. She has a certain boundary line in the world." Mrs. Angell reported improvement in Astrid's behavior, that she was less wild. Then Mrs. Angell and Mrs. Knowland agreed that the grandmothers were partly responsible for their daughters' antagonism, by backing them up.

In Session 85, Mrs. Angell reported anger at Astrid's behavior. Astrid maliciously spoke of Mrs. Angell's getting down to her level. In Session 86, Astrid said to Sally, "They will continue to nag while we are insane." In the next session she began talking of her own attitudes and problems and reported her problem in life as not being able to keep her mind off her boy friend. She stated that she saw a "silver lining coming up" on her mother's guilty face, but that she didn't care. Mrs. Angell earlier in the session had stated that if she looked back (to the past) she would get sick.

In Session 88, Astrid's murderous and suicidal feelings and need for tenderness and trust were evident. She stated, "I see what you mean, Hilda; I have the same problem in my life. I would like to kill her." Mrs. Angell then spoke of Astrid's ability to hold it in when her grandmother died. Astrid referred to herself as a boy acting like a girl.

In Session 89, when Mrs. Angell encouraged expression by Astrid, she spoke of running away or going to grandmother, as the only alternatives when things were bad at home. Mrs. Angell told of her own mother as overstrict on sex, and asserted that a mother should not impose herself on her child. Mrs. Angell and Astrid discussed control by mother as related to the self-destructive urges of Astrid.

In Session 91, Mrs. Angell spoke of her helpless rage at home, related to Astrid's absence. Astrid stated, "And cry about your mother's death." Mrs. Angell stated she was against idolizing a child. Astrid spoke of having her own bed, being alone, and loved. Mrs. Angell reported dreaming of people who were dead, just before Astrid got sick. Astrid shouted to mother, "You ought to have your nose busted."

In Session 92, Astrid cried, "And you come to the conclusion you want to commit suicide and don't know how." Mrs. Angell reported Astrid's incredulity on being in the hospital. Astrid bitterly retorted that it was a safe place to stay.

In Session 93, Astrid admonished herself in regard to loss of pride, humiliation, and not caring. She was sarcastic toward her mother, who was absent, as hypocritically solicitous.

In the last session, Astrid and Mrs. Angell had an intense interchange about whether Astrid would tell her age, like a good little girl, or not have a birthday party. Astrid rebelled, and mother and daughter went through several cycles of behavior, eventuating in reconciliation. At first Astrid was bitter about the punishing pressure mother put on her. Mrs. Knowland defended her. Astrid attacked her mother vituperatively, and mentioned killing mother when she was miserable. Mrs. Angell accepted the fact that daughter wanted to hurt her feelings. Astrid became recriminative, then spoke of lumping things that come through your life. Mrs. Angell blindly returned to insistence on Astrid's telling her age to the group, and Astrid intransigently asked her to kill her and indicated relinquishment of her own defense of needing to display happiness. Mrs. Angell was in tears and seemed to accept Astrid's feelings. She finally gave Astrid some cakes, which Astrid accepted sarcastically yet philosophically, "You finally got around to giving me some cakes."

This pair had gone through the preliminary interchange apparently necessary to working through their problems as mother and daughter. They seemed to have regressed to a fixation somewhere at the three- to five-year-old level, with a marked misidentification of roles. Astrid seemed to take on the ways of many of the people in her past experience—grandmother, father, mother, boy friends, etc.—in kaleidoscopic form.

The group experience seemed chiefly to have enabled them to approach many problems of their current relationship and accept previously unacceptable feelings. In this approach they faced some of their despair and anger relative to abandonment—Astrid on her hospitalization, Mrs. Angell on Astrid's deviation from her idealized image of self which included display of happiness to the exclusion of negative feelings. Their wishes to hurt one another became quite evident. Mrs. Angell showed less susceptibility to Astrid's maneuvers in this regard.

5. PARTICIPATION OF THE DOCTOR AND OBSERVER

As noted earlier in this work, the doctor studied the visiting-room group as a regular part of his investigation of the group phenomena in the hospital community. He was approached by the mothers of the group chiefly as an administrator. Part of this approach was undoubtedly in response in the situation to the inquiring (and to some extent, critical) looks he gave this group as he came and left the building. In addition, the doctor was the patients' group therapist, and the mothers related to him on that basis, exhibiting what appeared to be the characteristic ways of people who are excluded from an influential group.

The doctor was here in a situation to some extent similar to that of the mothers in regard to the ward therapy group. In the visiting-room group the patients were being influenced, and he was excluded. He noted his involvement in this regard as a sign that he was close to something that could with profit be looked into. He did so.

In that endeavor an internal decision was required. This involved estimation of his capacity to enter into an analytic relationship with this group, one in which defenses of the mothers, daughters, and doctor would be relinquished, and he would be called on to guide the inquiry into channels strange yet all too familiar to the most inaccessible and resistant aspects of his personality. The decision was made after several weeks of pondering, and chiefly on the basis of previous experience with group therapy, to the effect that the group members, as in the past, would help him out. Another preponderant factor was the experience in therapeutic work that he could trust the leads provided by the empathy experienced in a professional capacity, and by what at first seemed to be wayward emotions, in this case to enter into and control what was going on between the mothers and daughters, and to identify with the daughters.

Having made this decision he relinquished some of the distance, manipulative, judgmental, and evaluative aspects of his professional functioning, and committed himself to experiencing and working through the emotional situations in which he found himself with this group. This called for action to structure the therapeutic situation to accomplish these ends.

Control mechanisms, both interpersonal and intrapersonal needed to be subjected to analysis. The doctor abstained from *a priori* agreement with the mothers and daughters on their points of view, offering active support and guidance in the discussion of the reactions which ensued. The dependent, supervisory and resistant attitudes of the group members in regard to the doctor came out. The doctor worked to evoke the entire range of these attitudes, noting his subjective responses and the clues provided by the group dynamic as it unfolded. The mothers, on the basis of social consensus, were asking the doctor to join them in controlling their daughters. The doctor felt dragged between the two, and knew that he was in contact with controlling maneuvers important to the defenses of both mother and daughter. He recognized also that he leaned toward the daughters. Having identified his position in these regards he decided to realize it in the interpersonal situation.

Cutting away from the expected social usages and controlling ways of the members activated in the doctor the deepest anxieties of the experience. These anxieties were not as specific, or experienced as overtly as those which appeared later, but pertained to issues of great importance to this work: an encounter with strangers and survival of the group as a therapeutic instrument. These issues, especially the latter, were present throughout the experience; however, in the initial contact with this difficult and pioneer group it was touch and go as to whether therapy was possible at all, and the doctor abandoned by the group. These anxieties were manifest largely by the doctor in defenses of emphasis on selling purposefulness to the group. Along with this emphasis went a dependency on the purposeful, hopeful aspects of the personalities of the members and the members who displayed this type of defense. This to some extent served to slant the evolving mores of the group away from openly negative feelings, except for those expressed after the individual completely despaired. It also served, however, to carry the group members on faith, while they became accustomed to the ways of therapy.

Along with this defensive purposefulness genuinely educative therapeutic operations were engaged in. The procedure of evocation of what was on the minds of the members was repeatedly engaged in by statements like, "What do you want to talk about today?" or by sitting silent until the group members spoke up. The group soon accepted this necessary discipline.

In the initial situation of resistance to relinquishment of their accustomed relationship with an "authority doctor," the group, as described earlier, structured itself in a number of ways simultaneously; as mother-daughter pairs, as a mothers' subgroup, and as a daughters' subgroup. The mother-daughter pair was the prior one and the most durable, and from it arose an event of prime importance, the first overt commitment of feeling to the doctor, Laura's, when she was urged to have faith by her mother. The doctor himself found his first emotional commitment to be toward Hilda, one of the daughters, when her mother supervised her.

It is certain that the doctor's previous and continuing therapeutic relationship with the daughters in the ward group was a factor here. Of great importance was his identification with the daughters as a result of his anxiety on initial contact with the group, and the effect of the resistance of the mothers.

Of the elements in the group dynamism expressing the various identities and feelings of the members, the mother-daughter pairs, the mothers' subgroup, and the daughters' subgroup, the first came through with the most direct emotional communication. This was about an issue usually brought up early in institutional groups, but suggestively close to a prominent defense of the doctor at the time: faith in the doctor. The daughters as a subgroup held themselves aloof and resistant. Of the mothers' subgroup, the intellectual mother (Mrs. Knowland) allied herself with the doctor, in her enthusiastic yet distant way. Toward this he felt ambivalent, welcoming her support, yet recognizing it as a defense. The politician member (Mrs. High) represented herself and the other mothers about their daughters' problems, in accordance with polite social usage, then more directly, as the doctor abstained from their usages, and later identified with the daughters. Specific feelings related to nuclear issues in the treatment were being joined, and the problems to be worked out in treatment were becoming clearer.

The doctor found that these overt and specific feelings in a sense impeded therapy, though not seriously, and in another very important sense served as a constant indicator of the emotional situation in the group. This involvement was present in all the professional people who visited the group, to a varying extent. In some, it was so severe that they had to leave the room because of mounting fury or psychosomatic symptomatology. Most asked, after the session, "How could you stand it?" or, "Why didn't you do something to stop that mother from doing that to her poor daughter?"

When the mothers attacked the daughters, in their anxiety-driven ways—ranging in mode from a derogatory verbal barrage, through a smiling detachment, to a direct physical blocking of daughter's anticipated action—the doctor reacted with despair, then anger. He felt like reciprocating the maneuvers of the mothers, with derogatory, detached, and physically blocking ones. Suppression gave way to expression at times, as noted earlier. In the early months of the project, the doctor gave little orienting speeches on the difference between mothering and domination, and feeling guilty about the hostility behind this maneuver, accepted support from Mrs. Knowland who showed some antagonism, however detached, to the domineering ways of Mrs. High. Another sequel to his guilt about display of antagonistic emotions was some tendency to give in to the domineering mother by adopting her social usages and accepting her rationalizations.

These sidetracks from therapy, though they lessened the immediate tension in the doctor and group, increased the distance between him and the members who represented the dependent feelings of the group; as such they were unwise. Similarly, it is likely that the doctor's patient-like feelings toward their mothers pleased the daughters in one sense, but slowed their verbalizing on their own, since they had a spokesman, and worse still, left them feeling less secure about dealing with his dependency feelings in a close relationship with them.

Toward the defiance of the daughters the doctor experienced feelings similar to those of the mothers, but not as regressed and intense. He was moved toward putting down the passive sort of rebellion the daughters showed him and to get them to respond in a manner more consonant with his needs of the moment, of being good patients and speaking clearly of their feelings toward their mothers and himself. The doctor's feelings on this score were chiefly manifest at this phase in therapeutic maneuvers which, while dynamically sound, were somewhat obsessive in their drive toward the goals of the group. In this drive he brought at times disparate elements in the group together too soon, which lent itself to the mothers' maneuvers of forcing the daughters to talk because the doctor wanted them to.

The various emotional commitments on the part of the group and the doctor served, as the group survived and assimilated the experiences, to ease the tensions within the group, and permit the progressive eruption of responsibly voiced underlying feelings on the part of members of the group. The doctor was in this context freed to attend to further therapeutic operations. One of these concerned the impediments to communication between mother and daughter. In the ever-present situation where mother was wrought up over daughter's behavior, the doctor supported the mother, daughter, and group members in bringing out their feelings about the situation present at the time between mother and daughter. Through the range of associations uncovered each time, and the working through of attendant anxiety, the mother and daughter were helped to face and communicate their repressed feelings. Knowing something of the initial range of expression of the group, or its communication potential, the doctor worked for expression of the complete range of feelings on the problem of the mother-daughter pair by the group, and by the pair itself. If this expression was impeded or diverted, he sought to investigate the anxieties which led to the diversion. At such times he faced the choice of analyzing the relationship between himself and the members who were blocked or of that between the members. It seemed more appropriate on the whole to do the latter, and to lead the group back to the anxiety-laden situation. He reviewed the events that led to and stemmed from the point of anxiety, or simply noted that it had switched from the subject at such and such a point, and asked for associations to the event.

As in other group work the doctor repeatedly went through the experience of, by waiting a few moments, having members of the group come out with thoughts and feelings he was experiencing. In addition, these expressions, which had to do with the members' ego operations, when provided by the group were usually more pertinent, moving, and acceptable to the group. The members of the group evidently had greater empathic access to one another.

The doctor experienced some genuine surprises in the

course of therapy. The chief one was the revelation of the underlying dependent feelings of the mothers, their abject dependence on their daughters. A preconception the therapy had started with was that of freeing the daughters from the domination and "smother love" of the mothers. However, the guilt-ridden unceasing preoccupation of the mothers over the welfare of their daughters in time showed itself to be concerned with an intense need for certain kinds of responses from the daughters. This seemed, according to the mothers, to have been present since the birth of this child. There was something invested in the daughter of intensely personal meaning to the mother, which she could not relinquish.

The uncovering of this aspect of the mother-daughter relationship made guidance of the treatment process much easier, since it made the mothers more understandable. The doctor was able more clearly to define his identity in the group and through cognizance of his involvement to disengage from the resistance of both mothers and daughters, and attend to helping them face their feelings toward one another. He was able more readily to recognize the identity of the various subgroups, and of the manifestations of the mother-daughter sequences, and to help in their clarification and resolution.

As the members began identifying their previously dissociated dependent feelings, the doctor felt rewarded, and reconciled to the previously distant members. The simultaneous evolution of the mother-daughter sequences lent specific meaning to this process, inasmuch as there was some vicarious reliving of previously unfinished business within himself.

It became increasingly apparent on study of the data that in the group process the members, including the doctor, had undergone a significant experience. They had joined in exploring their personal involvement, or operating egos, from the level of social usage (both the usages of the accepted "normal" and of the alienated patient) into that of their dependent selves. This process of self-identification had been experienced on a group as well as on an individual level.

The relationship of the therapist and observer highlighted many of the mechanisms previously described. This was particularly manifest at the end of the session and the beginning of the postsession interview. The therapeutic session occurred at the end of the day and both the therapist and observer were fatigued and their dependent selves were close to the surface. The therapist brought to the interview his disappointment that his own and the group's idealized goals and aspirations had not been realized in the meeting, and the expectation that the observer would criticize him as he was already doing himself. The systematic review of the events of the meeting would not have been possible had we not guarded against acted-out involvement in this highly charged area, which related to the supervision of the therapist. This was achieved as a result of professional discipline, the mutual respect of observer and therapist for each other's ability, and integrity, and identification with the goals of the research and therapy. Also helpful here was the fact that the observer was not dependent, administratively, on the therapist, being on loan from another project. Thus we avoided some of the pitfalls which abort or severely hamper some research efforts, and which stem from acted-out rivalry and recriminative quarrels.

In the systematic review, the observer singled out for discussion events which were, first, very clear, in order to get a statement from the doctor of his therapeutic intent and of its rationale; and, second, those which were unclear, in order to get clarification of them. Both types of situations involved both the doctor's emotional involvement in the group and his therapeutic operations. Through this professional interchange the therapist and observer were able to acknowledge the experiences of the session and incorporate them for further use. This in practice occurred in a question's being raised; the therapist's re-experiencing in memory the therapeutic situation, with its attendant anxiety, but now in the context of the professional interview with the concomitant awareness of irritation, inadequacy and projected criticism, as well as pride and sense of achievement. There was some ventilation of these feelings. The therapist would then use these feelings as basis for free association about the meeting, and in this the observer would join him, and inferences would be arrived at as to the meaning of and relationships in the events under discussion.

In a similar manner the relationship of the doctor and observer during the sessions themselves was useful in highlighting problems in therapy. The relationship itself did not give rise to problems during the sessions. A problem arose in the group situation when members of the group, reacting to what was then going on in the situation, would act out this reaction by turning to the observer for attention or to show their suspiciousness through inquiry about what she was writing. The observer here represented an authority they could turn to, from the doctor, for understanding, and who also was putting down on paper potentially judgmental observations. Through this external representation in the observer of aspects of the doctor's functioning, data on the ego operations of the members were revealed to the doctor and observer as definite events in the group. Both the doctor and observer had seen and heard. The problem from then on was arriving at agreement on the nature, then the meaning of the event. For this the procedure would be as outlined above, with the observer in addition submitting her reactions as data for the drawing of inferences.

V

CONCLUSIONS

1. Interviews with Members of the Group

The procedure of the Group Psychotherapy Research Project usually included the evaluation of patients by psychiatrist, psychologist, and social worker before and after a period of therapy to see what changes if any had occurred. For practical reasons it was not possible to carry out this kind of program with the mothers' group at the beginning, but the observer interviewed the mothers and daughters at the time group observations were discontinued, and the doctor subsequently.

The data obtained through these interviews were intended to throw light on the following areas:

(1) how the mother-daughter relationship had been affected;
(2) effect of the group on family relationships;
(3) effect of the group on other relationships;
(4) effect of having the daughter in the group;
(5) reactions to the group.

History was not sought after except in an attempt to evaluate change in the mother-daughter relationship; but in a number of interviews the mothers brought up the history of the case spontaneously.

Six of the seven mothers who attended the group were interviewed. The seventh, Mrs. High, had moved to a distant city, and had also entered a negative phase in her relation to the group, and no arrangement could be made to see her. During the interviews with the observer, there was evidence of anxiety on the part of all the mothers, the anxiety becoming more pronounced when they talked of the patients' illness, despite the fact that a friendly though casual relationship had been present between the mothers and observer. Their freedom with the interviewer was indicated by mention of some negative feelings toward the therapy, other group members, and in one instance, the doctor. The social worker attempted to interview the patients, but because of their shyness insufficient data could be obtained from them to be useful in the research.

In interviews with the doctor, the mothers and daughters behaved differently than in the therapy situation. In many respects they reverted to the sort of relationships present early in the group experience. The interviewer was, in this light, again a psychiatric authority, to whom everything was told, who was assumed to be uncritical, yet was guarded against. He was assumed to be understanding, yet was looked down on as outside the pale of the mothers' grasp of the situation.

However, this reversion to dependency was only partial. The group experience had altered this situation somewhat. The mothers felt a fellowship with the doctor, and vice versa. Experiences had been lived through in the group which put the doctor more in the light of someone who was trusted as a fellow member of a group which had achieved an identity of its own. In this regard both of the interviewers were accepted as individuals to whom the group member could reveal her private anxieties. The mothers and daughters had been evidently prepared for individual therapy by the group experience.

2. Evaluation

There had been no cures in the sense of extensive reorientation of the individuals' life patterns, and concomitant contact with reality. The mothers looked about the same in appearance. The daughters were somewhat improved in dress and manner, but to superficial observation, very little change had been effected.

All of the mothers reported changes in the nature of their struggle with their husbands from a vague, generalized defense of each others' prerogatives to a more realistic acceptance of each others' feelings and position. They made less emotional demands on their husbands, appreciating that they had feelings, although they were not showing them, and that there was something to be said for the husbands' attitude that they could not afford to get upset because they had to go out and earn a living.

Three of the mothers (Mrs. Link, Mrs. Roper and Mrs. Angell) had, at the outset of therapy, been crying a good deal at home, and expecting their husbands to do something about their emotional state; another was very depressed. All reported that in one way or other they were controlling their feelings better. For example, the depressed one waited until her husband, who had his day off the day following the meeting, went to work before allowing herself to feel the depression which seemed to come with the meeting.

All had been impressed by the fact that during the period the group was meeting two of the husbands had died of heart attacks; they implied that emotional strain must have been a contributing cause to those deaths. The widowed mother interviewed, Mrs. Tenant, attributed her husband's death to grief over the patient's condition. The mothers uniformly reported intense reactions of loss on the death of Mr. High, consolation of Mrs. High, and subsequent lessening of their dependent demands on their own husbands. For instance, Mrs. Roper reported decrease of her bickering with her husband to get an emotional reaction from him when she came home frustrated and angry from her visit with Rae.

The mothers reported a greater awareness that their husbands and other loved ones might be taken from them. Other mothers, Mrs. Knowland and Mrs. Angell, stated that they were now easier on their other children, recognizing their untoward behavior (usually withdrawal) as motivated by anxiety. They reported that they tended less to raise issues about the family not caring for them. The husbands were reported as indirectly participating in the group experience. They apparently encouraged their wives' attendance and dependence on the group, and indirectly "got to know the members of the group." There had been much discussion (in several cases, while in bed) of the issues and personalities in the group. The husbands were apparently able to accept wife's dependence with less anxiety when dealing with her attitudes toward the group, rather than in relationship to himself or the sick child. Both husband and wife seemed to have talked constructively in the area of their feelings, and have less apprehension and condemnation and demands on each other.

The mothers reported changes in their relationship to their daughters. All of them seemed to be less beset with the feeling that they were not doing enough for their daughters. Some—Mrs. Knowland, Mrs. Angell, and Mrs. Roper—could show some negative reactions toward daughter without as profound guilt reactions. Daughter, on the other hand, showed (most clearly in Karen Knowland) a definite tendency to let go of mother, and greater warmth toward father. She was able to defy mother pertinently and on current issues when on visits home. Mrs. Knowland reported Karen's "putting her foot down" in relation to mother's overclose supervision of all her activities.

In discussing their relationship with daughter there was still a pronounced tendency to describe it in terms of daughters' fulfillment or failure to fulfill mothers' wishes, or the daughters' affection for the mother. For example, Mrs. Link helplessly complained of her daughter's calling the telephone operator and saying, "Call the police, I'm being neglected," and of daughter's preference for father. Two mothers reported an improved relationship because daughter was "sweeter" and "more open."

Three of the mothers, Mrs. Tenant, Mrs. Roper, and Mrs. Link, had a close physical tie to the patient before the onset of the illness, fondling and cuddling the daughter, often sleeping with her. They talked to the observer, both in the interview and in postsession conversations of how much they missed this physical contact. One of them reported that when the daughter was sicker, she, the mother, could not have sex relations with her husband. These three mothers now were jealous of daughter's newly developed interest in father.

These mothers stated their increased awareness of treating their daughters like babies. Mrs. Tenant expressed her "loving Tina too much" as a sin, for which she was being punished. Mrs. Angell resolved that "instead of smoothing things over, to go about a rehashing of upsetting things with Astrid, which is necessary to let them out." Mrs. Roper stated, "Everything doesn't now revolve around Rae." Mothers reported they felt free to skip a visit to the hospital, when it was inconvenient, or they were particularly resentful.

The group seemed to have in part replaced daughter as the focus toward which mother's thoughts and feelings turned in distressing moments during the day. This occurred most often when it or the mother missed a session. Five of the mothers indicated that they got emotional support from the group. They gathered at each others' houses at intervals. Four of them held long conversations over the phone during the week, and derived comfort from this and from being able to talk in the group. This apparently relieved the husbands of some of their wives' emotional demands.

The mothers reported differences in how they felt toward each other in and outside the group situation. They would ally with or resent other group members bitterly during the session. They all reported that after the session each felt a bond of fellowship: "We would do anything for each other." The alliances were apparently generally in the pattern described in Dynamic Correlations in the Group: Mrs. Tenant, Mrs. Link, and Mrs. Angell saw feelings very clearly, and did not understand the detachment of Mrs. Springer, Mrs. Knowland and Mrs. High. The latter three, for their part, attacked the others' blind spots—their open mothering of their daughters. Mrs. Roper straddled both groups. All reported that they were aghast at Mrs. Springer's open rejection of her daughter, and "appreciated" Mrs. High's furnishing of topics and speaking up to the doctor.

All were dismayed, as was most clearly expressed by Mrs. Knowland, by the doctor's "putting the responsibility right back on the mothers." Mrs. Knowland and Mrs. Angell reported their resentment at the group's leaving them flat when they expressed an opinion, gradually "examining the something that was amiss" with themselves at that point. Mrs. Knowland expressed it as "others responding to my tension, when I just sit there and smile, helplessly."

The mothers all expressed gratitude to the doctor. One of them brought out her guilt over the fact that she was benefitting by the group, when she thought it was supposed to be for her daughter. All of the mothers, except for Mrs. Springer, indicated relief of their feelings either of guilt or of stigma, attached to having their daughters ill and hospitalized. They could talk with friends and relatives about their daughters' hospitalization with relative ease, and with some positive feeling about what they and the hospital were doing.

Some material emerged indicating decreased anxiety in other relationships. One mother told of how she was now able to complain if given the wrong change, and to go out without being worried because the bathroom was not clean. Another spoke of her realization that in all situations she needed to keep relations smooth. A third stated that she was now sleeping, in contrast to the insomnia she had at the inception of the group; she attributed this, however, to the fact that she did a lot of housework and tired herself out. A fourth said she "used to blab everything," but had gotten so that she kept everything to herself and thought that her present attitude was: "Why make them miserable?" In a fifth case, the mother herself did not report change in her behavior, but the hospital personnel reported that for the first time in two years she had been able to sit down and give a coherent social history (this occurred after there had been discussion in the group of her inattention to other people).

All the mothers mentioned that having the daughters in the group gave them better understanding that their own daughters were ill through seeing the other daughters. The implication was that, until they saw other patients behaving the same way, they could not accept the idea that bizarre behavior came from illness. Two of the mothers (Mrs. Knowland and Mrs. Angell) verbalized a competitive feeling that their daughters were "better" or less sick than the others; and one of these mothers confirmed the impression of the doctor and observer that this competitiveness influenced her to cooperate with the doctor so as to get her daughter well faster than the others.

On the other hand, four mothers (Mrs. Knowland, Mrs. Link, Mrs. Roper and Mrs. Angell) were hesitantly critical of having the daughters in the group; one said that she was inhibited in speaking, either out of pity, or hostility about the patients, and three were upset by the behavior of the patients, two because they feared some violence, and the third because she felt that they upset her daughter.

Changes in relation to fundamental issues were reported by most of the mothers in most of the areas of their living. It was interesting that data along this line were furnished most readily about the mothers' relationship to husband and decreased sense of isolation from others. About their daughters, the mothers still spoke with a great deal of anxiety.

Interviews which the doctor held with the daughters obtained material quite pertinent to the immediate issue for them—the doctor's leaving. In the midst of their psychotic defenses they came out with the thought that was uppermost in their minds at the time. Hilda revealed her desire to be able to assert herself, especially with a man, in sexual intercourse. She bitterly resented "stuck-ups." Sally spoke with a great deal of despair of her unacceptability, and filthiness. Astrid vituperatively and reiteratively yelled at the doctor that he was going, never to come back. Rae alternately attempted to seduce the doctor and deny his presence. Tina laughed. Karen sat and held her breath. Laura told the doctor to go away.

In their behavior outside of the interview situation the daughters appeared to be improving. Laura and Karen were on extended visits. Karen showed great progress in her behavior at home. Her former behavior had disappeared almost completely, to be replaced by some overcompliance, which in turn was giving way to increased and pertinent self-assertion. Hilda and Astrid developed interest in ancillary therapeutic activities. All of the patients participated from time to time in birthday parties for the patient members in private homes or at the hospital. The dress and appearance of all the patients had improved, for which the mothers were particularly appreciative.

3. RESULTS OF THE INVESTIGATION

This report has scattered through it indications of the changes which occurred in the course of the group experience. None of these changes can be definitely proved to be due to the group itself. However, they seem to be related to the processes evident in the group; what is more, they seem to be an integral part of the process.

The most significant therapeutic result was the initiation of the process of therapy itself. There was serious doubt as to whether these people could be kept together in the same room. This was accomplished, and their co-operation enlisted in the investigation of their emotional involvement as individuals.

In their despair and resistance, the mothers recurrently stopped in the search into what was happening and turned to conjecture and assertions that heredity and organic defects had caused their daughters' illness. The investigation was carried through this despair and resistance into the interpersonal processes going on between mother and daughter, especially revolving about the issue of abandonment. Related important issues dealt with in the group were conformity to social modes, fulfillment of mother's expectations, contempt for each other, etc.

This was achieved not through indoctrination in psychological rather than hereditary causation, but through actual and increasingly conscious experiencing of the emotions attendant to the happenings in the group. It became evident that the interpersonal process present between mother and daughter played a part in the perpetuation of daughter's illness. This process, through therapeutic investigation, was altered.

The evidence for the alteration in the group has been presented in great detail in this report, through the medium of a play-by-play account of the group process. Since the investigation was chiefly concerned with the dynamics of the group, the relationships of the group members were not followed outside the group with an adequate plan and enough consistency to be considered from the standpoint of developmental patterns, as are the rest of the data. However, the terminal interviews of the social worker and the doctor with the mothers, and the estimation of the status of the patients based on interview and adjustment in the hospital indicate improvement in areas of living outside the group.

More immediately important than the therapeutic results were the lessons learned regarding the psychological processes experienced in the group setting. This study taught the investigators a great deal about the dependent ties of mother and child. It furnished data on group dynamisms and their relationship to therapy. The involvement of the therapist and observer was thrown into bold relief. Some data on family dynamisms, both operational and inferred, were obtained.

Alteration of the mothers' superior and dominating attitudes toward daughter was effected as current issues between them were faced and dealt with. This in turn permitted progress to be made in revelation of their feelings to each other. They then could share the feelings which had been previously forbidden to discussion. These were found to be both private and mutual.

Some data were obtained in reference to a number of basic questions on genesis and treatment which were encountered in the investigation. Was the daughter sick by nature or was the nurture in the family responsible? Why did this particular child fall ill? Should the method of treatment be an authoritative cutting of the tie between mother and sick child, or work on the relationship between them? Were mother and daughter hopeless from the standpoint of possible improvement through psychotherapy?

The evidence provided by the group experience was not conclusive, but pointed toward the importance of nurture. One indication lay in the change in the daughters as the mothers changed their mode of "nurture." This became apparent as the mothers became more able to face the adults in the group relative to issues present between them, and dependence and attentiveness to daughter became less pressing. Either as a result, or concomitantly, daughter responded favorably. As the nurture changed, the nature seemed to change.

This did not remove from consideration the probability that the daughters were significantly different from most girls from an early age. It merely pointed to the fact that there were psychological factors of reversible nature.

The question as to why this child and not the other children became ill likewise cannot be answered. The data obtained are relatively unreliable, since they stem from history, rather than operational investigation. In most of the histories obtained, that daughter was born into a situation in which the issue of abandonment of the child was highly relevant. In some the grandmother seemed to have to rival the mother for the patient's response, but not for other siblings.

The question of approach to the mothers' dependent tie was an ever-present one. It became apparent early that mother was dealing with something highly important to her own self in her attentiveness to daughter. Investigation rather than authoritarian severance of this tie seemed indicated. How to keep this investigation realistic constituted the real problem. The doctor's involvement and departure from realistic relationships when up against the question of whether mother and daughter would ever be strong enough to relinquish one another showed itself as an arrest in the therapeutic investigatory urge. The authoritarian position of knowing what was best for them—"You'll be better off without her"—seemed then to come to the fore. This stand became less prominent as the group's ego strength and the doctor's understanding of what he was going through grew.

This work has merely introduced the investigation of the problems of the members of the family in which there is emotional illness. The participation of the others in the family gestalt needs to be gone into. Identification of the intrapsychic as well as interpersonal mechanisms through concomitant individual and group analysis is highly indicated, for potentiation of therapeutic results as well as for more detailed information. Simultaneous sociological and anthropological study of these families is indicated, with comparative studies of families drawn from different social and cultural milieus. These studies could with profit be conducted along the lines of the present one, but for an entire (household) family, meeting in therapy regularly.

This study has demonstrated:

(1) That the interpersonal process present between mother and daughter in this type of family plays a part in perpetuation of daughter's illness.

(2) That this process can be investigated and altered.

(3) That the analytically oriented group-therapeutic process involved the group member's facing of her own problems as an individual, through mechanisms similar to those in the two-group of individual treatment.

(4) That the doctor's involvement in the interpersonal process has to be accepted as inevitable, recognized, and used as a clue to the solution of the problems in treatment.

(5) That reporting of group-therapeutic procedures on an operational level, while extensive, is feasible.

4. Inferences on the Interpersonal Process Between Mother and Daughter

The mothers were apparently deeply obsessive characters. In the group each related to her daughter to a great extent as an alter ego, who, when she conformed to mother's extremely rigid, unrealistic and idealized image of herself, was given tenderness and understanding. When the daughter deviated from this idealized image, the mother became anxious, and seeking to repress awareness of this concrete manifestation of her own low self-esteem and deviant impulses, rejected the daughter and lost awareness of the meaning of the daughter's communications. An intensification of the daughter's defenses against anxiety then occurred.

These aspects of the mother-daughter relationship seemed to be linked with the mother's relationship with grandmother and husband. The data available (clearest in the Angells, Ropers and Springers) on the relationship between mother and grandmother indicates an extremely intimate one where the grandmother took a dominant role in the raising of the daughter, abetting daughter in her efforts to control situations. This alliance seemed to have left its mark in the daughter's ability to exercise control later on.

It seems likely that when mother was submissive to grandmother or husband, the daughter was accepted as an alter ego and communicated to as a fellow sufferer. When mother exercised overt dominance in the interpersonal situation, the daughter was an impediment to be rejected.

Physiological functions, such as feeding, excretion, body-temperature regulation, sound making, movement, and postural tensions of the daughter all seemed in the group situation to have been observed minutely by the mother and to have very specific meanings to her. The performance of the daughter was watched, judged, and usually rejected. When she deviated from the specific mode of performance the mother required for her own equanimity at the moment or when she conformed, the daughter was (1) openly abandoned; or (2) awareness of her as a person, with human needs, repressed; or (3) openly condemned or fawned on.

The development of the daughter from the stage where her parents were to her awareness only extensions of her needs, seemed to have been hindered by channelization along the rigid lines of the idealized image the mother had of herself. As a result, the daughter's behavior seemed to have remained organized about the issues of infancy, the expectation of satisfaction or denial of her immediate needs.

The daughter's past history was strongly suggestive of the operation of strong repressions and reaction formation early in her childhood. The development of her ability to realize aspects of the other person outside of those which met or threatened her needs, seemed to have been greatly hampered. There seemed to have been a defect in communication on the part of the mother, in a way other than based on her own needs. The mother's communication to the daughter as an alter ego appeared to have hampered the development of the daughter's own ego. The evidence derived from the group process points toward a lack of tender communication on the basis of persistent, secure parental role fulfillment, or good experience. This left the daughter with very little patience. The appearance in daughter of a need evidently was followed, on the basis of past experience, quickly by the expectation of overfulfillment, or rejection on the basis of nonconformity to the idealized images of the parents.

The daughter, as shown most clearly in Astrid, seemed to have difficulty in distinguishing between herself and the parental figure who met her need of the moment. Perhaps there occurred an extension of her preverbal concept of self, abetted by a somewhat similar confusion on the part of her parents. The need seemed to call forth the image of the parental figure, which at the moment became the image the daughter had of herself. This misidentification led to images of self as of the opposite sex, or other age.

The attachment of the daughter to others seemed to be an extremely impulsive, possessive, "you-are-me" and "I-am-you" sort of thing, whether in relation to a person of the same or opposite sex. Of necessity, these feelings were repressed. In the area of thoughts on love, tenderness, and affection on the part of the daughter, there seemed to be a complete block, a plethora of thoughts on other people's feelings, or reaction formation onto another, compensating interest (both shown most clearly in Hilda).

The father in the family situation appeared to be related to quite intensely, colored greatly by the attitude of the mother to the father. The struggle seemed to be not so much one of the daughter for the parent of the opposite sex, but for the previously distant parent, seen in large part through the eyes of the mother. An example of this was found in Astrid who regarded her father from her mother's verbalized point of view, as an evil German. When the open psychotic break occurred, in most of the cases, data on the evil sexual intent of the father figure came to light, data which apparently reflected mother's attitude.

She saw the father, on the one hand, through her mother's eyes—a rigid authoritarian, or a bad, noncompliant sort of boy whom she could rail at—and on the other hand, as somebody who was interested in aspects of her ways not noted by or deemed uncommunicable or unworthy by the mother. Areas of communication and tenderness seem to have been opened up between daughter and father. However, the free alter-ego-like communication as with mother did not seem to have been achieved with the father.

Evidence pointed toward a repetition of the relationship with father in the "crushes" the daughter had with people resembling the father in overt or unconscious ways—in adolescence and later life, with the same or opposite sex. There were data on this in most of the cases, clearest in Sally's and Rae's involvement.

In the cases of several of the daughters, the daughter seemed to have the experience of overwhelming anxiety, the schizophrenic break, and the subsequent reshuffling of her ways, following an experience attended by a "crush." The profound anxiety of the experience could not be allayed by communication with the parents, with whom there had been so little to do except on the basis of conformity and repression, and there were few experiences and images of tender co-operation to fall back on.

The ways of the parents in their tense moments seemed to be the ones exhibited by the daughter, but in caricature and extreme form. The multiple images of the "parent-as-a-child" and the "child-as-a-parent" and the magical all-or-none omnipotence and impetuosity or sulking of the child became evident in the early stages of the breakdown. The phenomena of hallucination and highly autistic thinking, dissociation of affect, and inappropriate behavior appeared as the daughter was repeatedly disappointed and rejected through further lack of understanding by parents, relatives, authorities, doctors, nurses, attendants, and patients.

APPENDIX I

PROTOCOL AND ANALYSIS OF A THERAPEUTIC SESSION

This session may be considered as typical of the midpoint of therapy, where the earlier, more resistant, apparently chaotic sessions were giving way to the later, more coherent ones, in which the personal problems, and the mother-daughter relationship sequences stood out in bold relief.

The session protocol and the postsession interview are presented as taken down in shorthand by the observer. Added later in preparation of the final session summary were the inferences on the session dynamics and a schematic analysis of the session dynamics.

SUMMARY OF GROUP THERAPY SESSION 57

DR. ABRAHAMS' GROUP OF SCHIZOPHRENIC WOMEN

AND THEIR MOTHERS

DATE: March 2, 1949

PRESENT: Mrs. Springer, Sally Springer, and Miss Sheppard; Mrs. Roper, Rae Roper; Mrs. Tenant, Tina Tenant; Mrs. High, Hilda High; Mrs. Link, Laura Link; Mrs. Angell, Astrid Angell; Mrs. Knowland and Karen Knowland.

THERAPIST: Dr. Abrahams

OBSERVER: Edith Varon

PREMEETING NOTES: Observer arrived a few minutes early and had to wait at the door several minutes before anyone opened it. Hilda was standing in the corridor and looked out of the door at the observer but would not talk. Karen was waiting for her mother and told Mrs. High that she was "fine." Tina was sitting on her mother's lap looking in her mirror. Astrid was saying to her mother, "Hello, Mother . . . don't you match your brains with mine—ever," and she stalked out of the room.

OBSERVATIONS

INFERENCES

Astrid keynoted the rivalry existent between mother and daughter. She also signaled the form of ego relationships formed by the patients at this stage of the session. Her actual dependency in the hospital was a far cry from the acted-out rivalrous challenge displayed here. She evidently almost completely denied by implication caring what happened to her or for her personal responsibility in determining her future course. Part of this intransigent denial was based on a sort of bullying espousal, probably close to consciousness, of the cause of the wronged and abandoned patients.

(1) Mrs. High told the therapist that she asked Hilda if she wanted to ask Karen (who was standing out in the hall) if she wanted to come into the meet-

(1) Mrs. High here projected her own supervisory role-taking onto her daughter, who, on the basis of her role as a patient was able to oppose mother with-

ing and Hilda said, "No, that is Dr. Abrahams' job," and Hilda came in by herself. Karen meanwhile was standing outside the meeting smiling, and refusing to enter. There was a lot of buzzing in the group and general conversation.

(2) Mrs. High spoke complainingly to the therapist saying that Hilda told her she was going to drift from reality and think of Mrs. Long. "She really enjoys drifting from reality."

(3) Therapist asked, "What was the reality? She was with you at that moment?"

(4) Mrs. High asked Hilda, "Don't you want me to discuss it?" Hilda said no, and Mrs. High insisted. Astrid asked Mrs. High, "Why not put a green ribbon on it?" Mrs. High repeated Hilda's telling her that she was going to drift from reality and saying that she liked it. She said judgmentally, "That is deliberate, not involuntary." Rae at this point came in and closed her eyes and looked pained.

(5) Astrid and Sally laughed as Mrs. High went on discussing

out otherwise regressing. Karen's refusal was likewise "safe" for her.

(2) After reporting the gratifying aspects of her relationship with Hilda, Mrs. High again turned to her dependent complaints.

(3) The doctor focused on the mother's part in the reality of the mother-daughter relationship.

(4) Mrs. High escaped by shifting the focus to Hilda's motivation, which, apparently through a process of projection and selective attention, she identified as deliberate. The doctor's abstinence (from joining Mrs. High), and the patients' growing rejection of her anxious and dependent supervision resulted in exposure and gradual examination of her own, confused flight from her dependent needs to those of others.

(5) The daughters seemed to be identified together against Mrs.

OBSERVATIONS	INFERENCES
that *she* didn't feel she drifted from reality. Mrs. High then asked Hilda, "Tell us about it." Astrid giggled about "What this woman says?" Mrs. Link, Laura, Mrs. Knowland, Mrs. Tenant looked to Hilda. The daughters seemed to be identified together against Mrs. High's position. Mrs. High said that what Hilda did was different from what she did.	High's position, displaying their derogatory and hostile defenses against her dependent supervision.
(6) Therapist, "You say you don't drift from reality, you change your activity." Astrid laughed in a disturbing way.	(6) Doctor focused on how Mrs. High handled her own problem, indirectly defining the ego operations of both mother and daughter, to Mrs. High's disadvantage.
(7) Mrs. High said in her activities she enjoyed other people, but that Hilda was alone. Mrs. Springer said, "It's a phantasmagoria—can you spell that, Sally?"	(7) Mrs. High compared herself to Hilda in their ego operations, to Hilda's disadvantage.
(8) Miss Sheppard told Sally to listen to Mrs. High; meanwhile Mrs. Springer filed Sally's nails. Mrs. High said that if we could understand this we would be going places. She said in a rather pleased way that she was astounded by how much Hilda retained of what she read, "She retains more than I do!" And she gave a nervous laugh. "If	(8) When Miss Sheppard told Sally to listen to Mrs. High, Mrs. High praised Hilda. Perhaps the boost to her ego enabled her to acknowledge one of Hilda's powers, the one Hilda possessed in her phenomenal memory. Mrs. High here indirectly approached her own repressed, denied memories.

OBSERVATIONS

INFERENCES

we can help her to understand about drifting from reality. . . ." Mrs. Springer said she thought the patients got things from conversations on the ward. Sally meanwhile was staring at a picture.

(9) Hilda asked what time it was and Mrs. High asked why. Hilda said she wanted to go back. "What are you going to bring me Saturday?" Mrs. High asked: "Is that all you are thinking about?" Hilda asked the therapist about china plates and looked very much in contact with what was going on. Sally laughed. Hilda said she wanted to get to where there would be Negro patients. She said Miss Firestone was on 2B. Mrs. High, "Why?" Hilda, "She is deaf." Laura meanwhile talked to her mother. Hilda asked Mrs. Roper what doctor would be on tomorrow. Mrs. High asked critically what difference it would make. Hilda, "No difference. . . . If I'm good I will go to P Building. . . . I will go home with you." After a pause Hilda asked, "What is an insane asylum, Mrs. Link?" Mrs. High spoke up saying that she used to hate to use that

(9) Hilda talked in a way that got Mrs. High to demonstrate the very type of behavior she objected to in Hilda, showing that Mrs. High was not so superior or different. Hilda was also comparing her life with mother's and derisively approaching her own dependency on mother while asserting her own power to "take" the difficult life in the hospital.

word. "They are much kinder in calling it a mental hospital. Hilda apparently doesn't realize that is what this is." Mrs. Springer said she did not like the word "lunacy." Hilda said she wore a strong dress this morning and was proud of it. Mrs. High asked, "Bragging of it?" Hilda, "Bragging of it."

(10)

(10) A comparison of powers between mothers and daughters had been going on, marked first by Astrid at the start of the meeting, and here by Hilda "talking strong" as a point. The members of the group showed cognizance of the separate strength and identity of the other in this field of power operations, and later in the next cycle of exchanges between the Highs, of dependency on one another. This marked the approach of the main turning point of the session.

(11) Mrs. Springer asked Sally if something upset her this morning. Sally, looking down, said in a low voice, "No."

(11) Mrs. Springer, who ordinarily was detached from her daughter, seemed to recognize her on the heels of the Highs' interchange.

(12) Mrs. High, "How are we going to get into this?" Therapist recalled that she asked this

(12) Mrs. High, attempting to reconstitute her limited grasp of the reality of the situation,

last week. Mrs. High, "When a person is sick you don't see anything. . . . Well, I see little gratifying signs."

went back to her former dependently supervisory position, but gave Hilda some "credit."

(13) Hilda continued to talk to the therapist, "Are you coming Thursday or Friday? Why not Thursday? I would like you to come Thursday." Therapist explained why he could not come Thursday. Mrs. High asked Hilda why she wanted him to come Thursday and Hilda explained that on Friday morning there would be a conference on the ward and in the afternoon there would be a picture show.

(13) Here Mrs. High combined her denying and supervisory advances, with some acknowledgment of daughter's capacity.

(14) Mrs. High, "Where were we anyway. . . . What did you ask me?" Therapist, "We started talking about Hilda's saying she was going to slip away from reality and I asked you to talk about what she was going to slip away from." Astrid, Laura, and Rae were watching the therapist closely. He went on talking of how Hilda was talking about little elemental problems of living here on the ward and Mrs. High was thinking of something else and went along with Hilda, and Hilda humored her good-naturedly.

(14) Mrs. High found that she had slipped from control, to a dependent position, and asked for help. The doctor made thematic connection, also acknowledged Mrs. High's actual dependency in the situation with him. He then defined her relatively inappropriate ego operations, comparing them somewhat unfavorably with her daughter's.

(15) Mrs. High, a little flustered, suggested asking one of the other mothers. She turned to Miss Sheppard and asked, "How do you feel?" Miss Sheppard, "I have no thoughts right now."

(15) Mrs. High resisted and seemed to be seeking support against the doctor's interpretation from the other mothers, but didn't get it.

(16) Astrid meanwhile was talking to her mother and showing the therapist her report card. Mrs. High asked the therapist for his opinion. Astrid said to her mother, "I was never sick! You dumped me over to a truck, took my clothes away, two grown men with white hair— none of your affair at all!" Hilda was now standing at the door.

(16) Astrid, in her relationship with mother, expressed what probably was the recrimination underlying Hilda's teasing of mother, and from which Mrs. High was defending herself. That this outburst by Astrid occurred when Mrs. High turned to the doctor was of note. Castigative and recriminative outbursts by the daughters to their mothers when any of the mothers appealed to the doctor were frequent.

(17) Mrs. Springer asked if the patients understood "each other better than we do." Mrs. High answered her, "Dr. Abrahams seems to feel that way. . . . I have often wondered."

(17) Mrs. Springer, who had at one time been psychotic, approached the interpersonal meaning of the daughter's position, understanding what it meant to be alienated. This approach was a distant one, however, and in character referred to relative adequacy and power.

(18) Mrs. Knowland and Karen now entered. Mrs. Knowland sat on the arm of the observer's chair and Karen sat near Miss

(18) The two subgroups, having in their own way squared off and tested each other's mettle, now began serious communica-

Sheppard (for lack of better eating space). Karen looked well, her eyes were bright. She bent over and sat rather hunched.

(19) Therapist to Mrs. High, "You ask, 'How do I get into my daughter's life?' "

(20) Hilda, "Have you ever been to the frigid zone, Mother?" She gave a little laugh and Mrs. High said she would like to make realism more attractive to Hilda. Mrs. Angell said that daydreams become more attractive.

(21) Mrs. High asked Mrs. Angell about what she would do. Mrs. Angell said she would do something, but she might day-dream—she would love to read. Mrs. High talked about using time productively, living in a world with normal people.

tion as individuals, and mother-daughter pairs, with mothers identifying with the daughters.

(19) The doctor guided Mrs. High toward facing her dependency on her daughter. In doing this the doctor intended to bring out and at the same time help bridge the intense power struggle about who should give in first. It was perhaps through this intermediate, less anxiety-fraught intervention that the doctor enabled Hilda to come out with her subsequent approach to her mother.

(20) Hilda's approach was one step removed from direct interpersonal meaning through metaphor; in addition, it carried a rebuff.

(21) The mothers were speaking for the dependent experience, within the context of the mothers' subgroup, in contrast to Mrs. High's "normal" ways of purposive relationship with normal people. Mrs. Springer's commitment was characteristic,

OBSERVATIONS

Mrs. Springer observed that a sick person's mind doesn't work like a normal person's. She looked around the room and asked, "Has anyone here had a breakdown? Well, I did." She then said that the things you loved to do you were unable to do. Mrs. Roper questioned her about how long her breakdown had lasted. Mrs. Springer, near tears, said that it had been a year or two. . . . that mental strength comes as a physical strength comes.

(22) Mrs. Knowland said that if you were in a place where you felt that people had given you up, that would make you worse, and you would lose your power of concentration. Mrs. Springer, about getting well, "You do that yourself." She said that here they didn't get the chance. Mrs. Link and Mrs. High discussed the percentage of patients that get well, and Mrs. Springer in a challenging voice said, "In spite, not because of treatment."

(23) Mrs. Angell talked to the therapist and Mrs. Link asked the therapist if Laura seemed

INFERENCES

in that she came out with an extreme exposition diametrically opposite to Mrs. High's ideas. She also carried Mrs. Angell's weak daydreaming, a way similar to Hilda's and regarded with contempt by Mrs. High, a long step further. In taking this essentially masochistically rebellious position within the mothers' subgroup, she placed herself in a dependent position. Having done so, she righted herself by maintaining the image of herself as intransigently getting well in spite of treatment.

(22) Mrs. Knowland, for whom concentration was quite important, joined her, in a general noncommitted sort of way.

(23) In this movement the group "reached" the doctor through two appeasing members, Mrs.

as active and alert. Therapist said no, Laura seemed very depressed. He didn't know what it was about because she hadn't talked with him. Mrs. Link said she didn't think it was anything on her part. Cheerfully she said that when she took Laura home she was not interested in a thing.

(24) Therapist observed that this was like Hilda, when her mother wanted to get into her life she talked about a frigid zone. He said Laura was hot tempered, now she was cold. Laura, "I don't care for the doctor." Mrs. Link urged Laura to continue but Laura refused. Mrs. High asked the doctor rather incredulously, "Do you think the frigid zone has something to do with the conversation? In conversation we got to the question of geography and I facetiously suggested a trip to Greenland—how do you feel that it ties up with this conversation? I think it was a coin-

Link and Mrs. Angell, by way of on the surface nonprovocative questions about daughter. The doctor's avoidance of direct confrontation of the challenging mothers was of note. In avoiding them he engaged in an operation in common with the mothers, turning to the dependent other, in this case, the daughters. The aspect of the relationships of the dependent other selected for attention was, paradoxically, the resistive, rebellious ego, as represented by a patient.

(24) Of the patients representing this aspect of ego relationships, Laura was the one turned to. Unlike Hilda, who spoke like a politician of tin plates and the doctor's place, Laura spoke simply of her distaste for the other person, frequently in oral terms. The doctor drew sparks of hostility from her, the hostility the mothers couldn't reveal.

cidence." Therapist pointed out that Greenland is a cold country. Mrs. Springer observed that it was a bitter-cold day today. Hilda was watching alertly.

(25) Therapist asked Mrs. High if green was not her favorite color and said that for her to take a trip to Greenland was not just a coincidence, "It's the land of your favorite color." Sally spoke in a very low voice to the therapist, "What about your shoes, want a special pair of shoes?" Miss Sheppard observed that Sally had a pair of green shoes. Therapist asked Sally why she didn't say this directly to Mrs. High. Sally stared at the therapist. Mrs. High said that she did have a pair of green shoes and Sally then leaned back. Mrs. High went on talking of liking green.

(26) Mrs. Knowland asked: "Is it desirable to enter into someone else's life, or would you let the person know that you are in readiness when the person wants you?" Mrs. Link said that was what she tried to do.

(25) The doctor, taking Mrs. High's cue, guided the group into association based on the meaning of words. This semantic association culminated in oral associations by Laura and Mrs. Angell, two members who next to the Tenants, had more direct access to their dependent feelings.

(26) Mrs. Knowland here opposed Mrs. High regarding entering into a person's life. She also assumed a responsible role, a prominent defense of hers, and brought the group back to ego relationships, as opposed to indulgence in indirect symbolic equivalents.

OBSERVATIONS	INFERENCES
(27) Laura talked about having blisters inside her mouth. Therapist said he wondered what that had to do with entering into a person's life. Laura started to say, "Where do they come from?" and stopped suddenly. Therapist asked for her feelings. Laura did not speak up.	(27) Laura expressed her negative attitude toward the experience of dependency in symbolized oral terms. The doctor brought communication back to an ego level, to bring out her feelings.

(28) Hilda repeated, "Frigid zone, Mother." Mrs. High said, "What about it?" Hilda, "It's cold there." Mrs. Angell spoke to the therapist about blisters being connected with upset stomachs.
Mrs. Springer asked where Laura would like to go on a trip. (This was the beginning of a movement to ask all the patients where they would like to go on a trip.) Laura named the Grand Canyon. Mrs. Springer asked Sally who said she would like to go to California this year. Mrs. Angell asked Astrid who named South America. Rae leaned on her hand and said she wanted to go no place. Miss Sheppard asked, "You like it here, Rae?" Rae, "Uh-huh."
Sally told the therapist that she was "The cat and the bat." Therapist asked her how it

(28) Hilda, then Mrs. Angell and Mrs. Springer led a movement away from direct interpersonal issues to an action and also geographical representation of relatedness.

ended. Sally's reply could not be caught. Miss Sheppard asked her for details.

(29) Therapist said that he thought Sally was talking about a wild goose chase and that she got the wrong bird. Sally, "The bird ate it." Tina looked at the group, then turned back to look at herself in her mirror. Mrs. Knowland asked Karen where she was thinking of going. Astrid told her mother she liked South American music, the tango. Mrs. High asked Hilda about Greenland and her reasons for wanting to go there. Sally talked to Miss Sheppard about a wild goose chase.

(29) The doctor utilized action-symbol language with Sally to link with interpersonal issues (the pair's and group's "wild goose chase").

(30) Mrs. Knowland asked in her thin distant voice, "Are we ready for something a little different? . . . What should a home give to people as opposed to an institution that gives warmth, medical care, treats them as immature—what should a home give?" Sally, speaking very low, "I will say this . . . and wake up." Mrs. Roper said, "What we haven't already given."

(30) Mrs. Knowland, taking to her defenses again, assumed the responsible role, by this maneuver keeping herself under control, putting others in their places. She brought the group back to consideration of ego relationships, also accusing the mothers.

(31) Mrs. High said that everyone responds to affection. Mrs. Angell responded sharply that

(31) The mothers responded with vague allusions to guilt over the past, and the daugh-

some people don't. Mrs. High was near tears. Astrid said sharply to her mother, "Don't tell my secrets!" Mrs. Angell said that she thought that if we talked Astrid would get well. Astrid began to act flippant.

ters with reference to talking, waking up, and secrets from the past, a foretaste of recrimination to come.

(32) Mrs. High asked the therapist, "Would you like to answer Mrs. Knowland's question?" Therapist, "What is happening here? Mrs. Roper says she would like to have Rae at home. As far as she can see she is giving affection and her daughter is turning away from her. Hilda talks about the frigid zone. Laura talks about not liking the doctor. . . . Let us see what goes on between the mother who feels she is giving affection and the daughter who reacts as to poison. What could be going on?"

(32) Mrs. High as usual referred to another person, this time the doctor. In a recapitulative interpretation, partly motivated by antagonism to her denying ways, he recognized but did not inquire into her resistance. Instead, he referred to the ego relationships of the mothers and daughters. The members responded in time by feeding him answers, in accordance with interpersonal issues of particular importance to each. The contributions added up to an exposition of the processes in the daughter of emancipation and achievement of identity, chiefly through denial of dependency.

(33) Mrs. Angell said that that was so puzzling. Mrs. High said that she imagined the daughter had some grievance. Sally laughed and watched the group. Mrs. Springer said, "The young may think their elders are not adequate." Mrs. Roper said of Rae, "She turns to her father

(33) Mrs. High led the group in "giving the daughter credit," recognizing their separate independent identity, while "giving in" on the issue of the parent's fault, a step toward entering the much-resisted state of dependency on the daughter (and doctor).

now." Mrs. Knowland remarked that it is usual in any growing person to stop relying on one's parents.

(34) Mrs. High began to talk about one's reaction to receiving an outward expression of affection from people you really didn't like. She said that she had had that experience of being showered with kisses and so forth from people she didn't like, and she described her discomfort. She concluded, "Whatever has caused the rift between our daughters and ourselves, we shower them with affection." Mrs. Angell said of herself that she didn't want affection. When her mother died she didn't want anyone to touch her and maybe it was the same thing with the daughters. The group was very quiet. Sally laughed painfully. Mrs. Springer spoke to Mrs. Link about things that Laura did. Mrs. Link told how Laura would not go into the yard after she got home. Mrs. Angell told Astrid that if she wanted to pay a visit home she would have to talk to Dr. Abrahams about it. Astrid was very quiet. Mrs. High, continuing her train of thought, said that sometimes

(34) Mrs. High and Mrs. Angell began revealing their reactions to disappointment. They came out with the feelings underlying the transformation from the dependent child—the underlying transformation of love and mutuality into anxiety and separation. This might be formulated as: "Since you denied me dependency and left me, I will distrust anything that connotes my need for you, and keep my feelings and self to myself, turn to somebody else (somebody else's person and feelings), go somewhere else!" The problem of "not knowing" the other in their accepted capacity—as mother, husband, etc.—prominent in the schizophrenic and manifested in the neurotic as name forgetting, is related to this situation of deprivation and recriminative anti-dependency.

you change your mind and like a person whom you have disliked before.

(35) Mrs. Springer said that sometimes you go back to your original feeling. She thought that it was customary for a person who is mentally ill to give them an entirely new environment. They might feel unwanted; there might be too much or not enough love and they need an altogether new environment. She turned to Mrs. Roper as she said that "patients are beginning to feel inferior with those around them. That's a very terrible feeling, that you can't keep up." Mrs. Knowland spoke of the need to be careful in returning patients from the hospital to their homes. Mrs. Springer agreed, "I would say so—sometimes they never return them to their homes." Mrs. Angell said Astrid wouldn't be going back to the same house because the family had moved. She would go to a new school. Astrid said to her mother, "You mean your son." Mrs. Angell rebuked her, "Don't talk like that, in daydreams." Astrid smiled smugly.

(35) Mrs. Springer moved the patient right out of the house (her own course during her psychosis). Combined with this note, she presented to Mrs. Roper, the mother who related as submissively inferior, her view of the patients' low self-esteem.

OBSERVATIONS	INFERENCES
(36)	(36) The Angells related to this material in an old pattern; mother exhorted daughter, who responded by denying and altering her mother's identity; and then mother rebuked her daughter, calling her a dreamer.
(37) Mrs. High said that she felt like a surgeon with a cancer or a tumor: "Dig the thing out."	(37) Astrid's provocative pointing out of some hidden but important aspect of her relationship with mother (being considered as a son) resulted in recurrence of impulses of denial, then extirpative impulses on the part of the mothers. These extirpative impulses possibly have some relationship to sexual and oral needs.
(38) Rae laughed.	(38) Rae's laughter may be taken as presumptive evidence that something important had been touched on.
(39) Mrs. High continued, "What can I do to make the life I know more attractive to her . . . . my hands are tied." Therapist asked the group: "How does the group feel about this 'dig the thing out' reaction of Mrs. High's?" Mrs. Link said she would love to. Mrs. Springer disagreed, saying, "It's putting something *in*." Miss Sheppard said it was not a question of dig-	(39) The doctor threw Mrs. High's question to the group, and the effect was a round robin discussion of methods of changing the patients' ways of dealing with the dependency feelings discussed earlier, now again considered as alien to the mothers' egos.

ging but it was more like crossed wires and a matter of getting them strung up right.

Mrs. High said it was because Hilda said that about drifting into fantasy. "She liked it and I thought if I could get rid of that cancer, make her feel that there are so many nice things in life . . . . what are you going to do with a person like that? She has as good as told me to mind my own business and she is right."

Mrs. Springer agreed with Mrs. High that you would "dig it out like a rotten spot in an apple." Miss Sheppard went back to her simile of crossed wires. Mrs. High asked what you would do with crossed wires. The group began to talk all at once with animation. (40) Mrs. Knowland said that if it was like a tumor, then you would dig it out, but that you needed to be careful what you compared with. Mrs. High said that it was of such long duration that it was malignant. Mrs. Knowland, "But is it malignant?"

(40) This animated discussion involved open contradiction of one another by the mothers on approaching the daughters' "rotten" resistance to their advances. The rising note of the interaction may be related to open ego relationship between the mothers, involving mutual support and competition. The animation also may indicate anticipation of success in dealing with this most difficult of emotional states, the dependent reaction to abandonment.

OBSERVATIONS

INFERENCES

(41) Therapist, "Let us look . . . . Mrs. High has a way of talking . . . . if someone should dig the thing out how would we feel?" Mrs. Roper said, "We would resent it, I guess, wouldn't we?" Mrs. Knowland said that she would say she needed to have something dug out of her.

(41) The doctor brought the discussion back to relationships with daughter. Mrs. Roper compliantly supplied an answer and Mrs. Knowland masochistically switched with daughter as the recipient of extirpation. The latter action casts further light on the nature of the empathy Mrs. Knowland has shown for the daughters' plight, especially Hilda's as a sort of masochistic defiance of the other mothers, and overcompliance to the doctor's sentiment, in all a basically regressively expressed defiance.

(42) Mrs. High, "You are right, but I'm mellowing with age; I'm looking myself over." Hilda, "What time is it, Dr. Abrahams?" Therapist, "Ten of five." Mrs. High said, "The sad part of it is that Hilda likes that drifting." Therapist, "We have gone off again . . . . someone said she would resent it. Are there any other feelings?" Mrs. High asked what the alternative was, "Leave her there?"

(42) Mrs. High's compliance seemed to be expressed as a contemplative process new to her in the group, and a temporal note. This seemed to bring on Hilda's question on time and disjunction, followed by Mrs. High's disjunctive action.

(43) Mrs. Knowland said this was not necessarily so and Mrs. High asked Mrs. Knowland to

(43) Mrs. Knowland's intellectual bridging of the disjunction led to the important concept of

tell us. Mrs. Knowland said you might have communication with someone who was lost and have information that would lead her to find her own way; or you might both be lost and find a way out. Mrs. Angell, "Yes, that's what I think." Mrs. High, as if giving in, "All right, dig up another path." Mrs. Springer began to talk about getting more calcium into the patients' brains.

(44) Mrs. High jumped on Mrs. Springer, "That's the complaint department, Mrs. Springer!" Mrs. Springer denied this, and said she always harped on this. The meeting fragmented. Mrs. High continued to say she wanted to get to the bottom of this. Hilda walked out, rang for the nurse and looked provocative. She kissed the wall while saying, "Nahh, nahh, nianny!"

(45) Therapist asked what the path was. Mrs. High, he said, asked Hilda to do something and Hilda mocked her and Mrs. High sat and looked disconsolate. Therapist asked if anyone had another path to offer.

(46) After a pause Mrs. High asked the doctor: "Why can't

both mother and daughter as lost. Both needed to find their way out. The more openly dependent mothers gave in to this idea, but Mrs. Springer presented an alternative concept by reverting to organic determinants.

(44) Mrs. High, as she did with her daughter when Hilda "talked crazy," attacked Mrs. Springer, when Mrs. Springer made the same kind of point Mrs. High had until recently. Hilda significantly responded by her provocative turning-a-way-to-something-else behavior.

(45) The doctor again referred to the relationship between Mrs. High and Hilda as it had been revealed in this meeting.

(46) The result of (45) was controversy among the mothers on

you give us another path. . . . I can't find it. . . . We are helpless." She smiled girlishly, saying, "I can't find a new path." Therapist asked if that wasn't part of the difficulty, Mrs. High's feeling that she hadn't enough mind. Mrs. High, "Umm humm." Therapist asked why; Mrs. High, "I haven't enough knowledge." Mrs. Knowland, "It isn't enough knowledge, is it? We went over that a year ago, that we use intellectual concepts too much, that it is a thing of the spirit."

their approaches. Mrs. High "gave in" on the issue of change of self, representing the mothers' wish for help. The pivotal point in this controversy was the question of knowledge or mental power. This appeared to be the anxiety-allaying article they lacked, for which they envied and attacked others, and for its lack attacked themselves. Mrs. Knowland's intellectually based, only apparently responsible approach to interpersonal problems was pitted against Mrs. Springer's highly symbolized and distorted referral of the problem to daughter's calcium (suggestive of hardness, as in bones). This element of anatomy had been important to her athletic defenses against anxiety in her youth. Mrs. High related to Mrs. Springer's ego operations as basically dependent and querulous, again seeing through defenses which were recently very much her own.

(47) Hilda, "Dr. Abrahams, I am not going to stay in Two Building all my lifetime." Therapist, "We are trying to work out another path, Hilda." Miss Sheppard and Mrs. Knowland were talking about

(47) Hilda talked of getting well (as opposed to slipping from reality) at the point where her mother had been admitting weakness and Mrs. Knowland had suggested abandoning intellectual defenses.

whether the daughters were intelligent enough. Astrid was saying to her mother, "I don't see why you can't take me home." Hilda was out of the room ringing the bell. Tina laughed. Mrs. High tried to coax Hilda back. Hilda repeated that she didn't want to stay in Two Building all her lifetime. Therapist recapitulated to Hilda the discussion on the need for a new path. Hilda walked out while he was saying, "Couldn't we look at what path you want your mother to follow right now." Mrs. Knowland commented, "That means it is none of her lifetime." Mrs. High said miserably of Hilda's going out of the meeting, "That can go on for a lifetime." Therapist asked Mrs. High what she would feel and what she wanted to say. Mrs. High hesitated, finally said she wanted Hilda to discuss the problem with the doctor. Therapist, "Anything else?" Mrs. High said, "No." Therapist asked if anyone else in the group had an idea. Sally, "Steaks, food." Therapist, "Yes, it's time to eat."

Meeting broke up.

THERAPIST-OBSERVER INTERVIEW

Therapist observed that this was a relatively easy meeting for him. The relationships were more open and direct, with and between the members. The trend of lowering of defenses by the mother and daughter continues.

Relationship today with the mothers appears to be that of obsessives with character resistances; they are either compliant, self-righteous, or no good, can't do anything. In this session, the patients' resistances seem to be bound up in selective attention to the mothers' lack of contact with the reality of their own dependency feelings. In addition, they feel that everything that goes on is tied to them, an act of some kind. Sally probably feels that everything that is said is set up by the doctor or by authorities.

The meeting was keynoted by Mrs. High's question of slipping away from reality and mothers wanting to stick to reality but finding a different path. Mrs. High is now willing to modify her terms of request for gratification to come from daughter.

Therapist expects the meetings to continue the cycle of the present one, starting with examination of the situation between the mother and daughter, regressing, going back to the therapist for help, and then going on by themselves. Mrs. High is beginning to see she couldn't live through her daughter.

The discussion of travel, though an escape from the interpersonal issue, was a collective way the mothers had of getting the daughters to talk. Therapist conjectured that the mothers may work collectively on their daughters, tell them how much they hate certain ways of theirs.

Therapist observed that Hilda in talking of the ward was talking as a patient on her own terms. She was talking realistically to her mother, that is, realistically from the standpoint of a hospitalized person.

Ward group: Rae Roper has been carrying on an active love affair with another patient with whom she makes physical love promiscuously. Rae is the sexual aggressor during the meeting and then she looks plaintively and guiltily at the therapist after the meeting. She seems more appropriate in her behavior, acts at times like a hellcat in defending her rights to magazines, etc. At times her aggression carries over into breaking things, for which she has been reprimanded by patients. She cries then.

Karen sat hunched over doing nothing or working on jigsaw puzzles. Hilda walked in and out, sat near the therapist, said she was thinking of Mrs. Long. She said something of hating her mother. Others talked about Hilda and about liking her; they emphasized dislike of Hilda's way of hitting her chest and screeching imprecations at herself.

Astrid sat and giggled. She expressed extreme antagonism toward her mother in the group discussion of attitudes toward mother and father.

Tina laughed less, seemed more pertinent and serious.

Laura was quite distant; seemingly pointedly so.

OUTLINE OF SESSION 57

Because of its importance in this group study, in this outline of the session, how the people got into relationships, committed themselves, was especially followed. All of the people in the treatment situation were committed in some way, if only by their physical presence in the treatment room. How, and under what auspices they committed themselves, on their own volition, for realization of their own purposes, were among the questions for study. This problem of realization of self, of responsible self-determined participation forms the keynote of this outline of the session.

As elsewhere in this study, description of the participation of the individual in the interpersonal or ego context called for the use of words and ideas belonging to that context, words like commitment, responsibility, success, failure, representation, operation, maneuvers, supervision, dependency, etc. These words denote the state of the interpersonal relationship of the moment, for the individuals and group.

In presenting this schema of the session a brief review of formulations presented earlier in this study is indicated. At the outset, the mothers and daughters were there for the other to get something out of it, and to guard against the other's behavior and person. Though the mothers showed extremely determined and able selves through their various maneuvers of supervision and social compliance, it was, as in every session from the very inception of the study, readily apparent that these actions, words, and feelings were determined by others. The daughters, likewise, were not committed for themselves, but through denial of others. Whereas the mothers spoke the words and followed the ways of society, again with nothing but indirect or blocked reference to themselves, the daughters as rigidly adhered to the patients' peculiarly individualistic, but still stereotyped language and ways.

Both were not responding to their own primary needs and impulses, were not responsible to themselves. Both did not ask and seek from themselves. The mothers in doing so would be going against the accustomed and accepted ways of their society, and even more personally, would be putting themselves in a position of dependency on their daughters, the doctor, and other group members. Much of their personalities had been organized around avoiding this state of dependency. Responsibility to themselves and others was present and voiced through the representations of others' selves as if they were the individual's own. This occurred on a critical, evaluative, and idealistic basis, and showed as defenses against realization by the individual of her own personal participation in the situation at hand.

These notions provide starting points for following the commitment of the individual in the group process, and of the evolution of the group about these nexal problems. This detailed study is only a crude start in the study of the phenomena of interaction of related individuals, as they come to grips with the forces that keep them apart, and at the same time learn to achieve their own separate identities.

I. Introductory power struggle over recognition of the other's separate identity.

   A. Implicit disavowal of own responsibility. Content revolved about relative power of the individual. Preliminary commitment through the others' ego operations.

      (1) Mothers made supervisory advances, daughters rebuffed them on the basis of their implicitly consensual, alienated patient identity. (1)*

      (2) Doctor abstained from support of the mother who usually represented the dominant attitudes of the mothers' subgroup (called in this outline the representative mother). (3)

      (3) Daughters vaguely identified together, acting as patients against representative mother's supervision of daughter. (Daughters had still not explicitly entered the discussion as patients.) (5)

   B. Beginning commitment on a rivalrous basis, coupled with acknowledgment of separate identity of the other.

---

* Numbers in parentheses at the end of sentences refer to corresponding section of Observations.

(1) Doctor guided the representative mother to consideration of her ego operations with daughter. (6)

(2) Mothers contrasted their ego operations with their daughters' to daughters' disadvantage. (7)

(3) Beginning acknowledgment of daughters' identity—on the basis of covert rivalry between the mothers.

    (a) Representative mother asserted daughter's assets (in contrast to another mother who played her daughter down). (8)

    (b) Mother rivalrous to the representative mother claimed daughters' ability to "get things" (understanding).

(4) Commitment (as acted-out rivalry) *by daughter* as a member of patients' subgroup. She presented her dependent self through her identity as a patient, yet in a denial mode of presentation (bragging, facetiousness about conformity). (9, 10)

(5) Acknowledgment of her own daughter's dependent feelings by mother rivalrous to the representative mother. (11)

C. Recapitulation of stages A and B juxtaposed, with fragmentary representation by daughter of direct dependent relationship with mother.

(1) Mother made supervisory advances to daughter combined with some acknowledgment of patient's separate capacities; daughter definitely related in a patient's capacity. (12, 13)

(2) Mother called on doctor for guidance; he related her to the ego operations of herself and daughter, emphasizing the relative appropriateness of daughter's. (14)

(3) Mother appealed to the mothers' subgroup, was abandoned. (15)

(4) Another daughter, by implication denying her present real dependency and her own part in the genesis of her situation, related to mother on the issue of her abandonment by mother. (16)

(5) Mothers moved to acknowledge the daughters' capacities (as a patients' subgroup) and their own lack of understanding. (17)

Having, on the basis of their developing identity as members of mothers' and daughters' subgroups, attained some operating concept of themselves and others as separate persons, the members of the group as mother-daughter pairs were able to turn to their problems in depending on one another.

II. Communication of Dependency on One Another.
A. Indirect Representation of Dependent State.
    (Maneuvers, representation through symbols and action still stand between the individual and the person on whom she depends.)

(1) Doctor guided the (still) representative mother toward relationship with her daughter. (19)

(2) Daughter made symbolized overture toward mother. (20)

(3) Movement toward direct relationships between the mothers and daughters through the medium of the mothers' subgroup and the doctor.

   (a) Mothers as a subgroup approached the experience of alienation and defenses against it, culminating in the exposition of her psychosis by a mother with marked intellectual defenses, and who exhibited marked masochistic rivalry. (21)

   (b) Indirect commitment of negative attitudes

toward help, medical and otherwise (members were speaking in general, addressing themselves to the mothers, rather than to the doctor as such). (22)

(c) Appeasing mothers addressed the doctor as an administrative authority about their daughters' state of mind. (23)

(d) Doctor linked daughters' ego operations with those of representative daughter. (24)

(e) Brief, direct relationship between doctor and daughter whose dependent feelings were most readily available in the therapeutic relationship. (24)

(4) Guidance by doctor of symbolic communication by group members. (25)

(5) Alternative supervisory guidance by intellectual group member to interpersonal relationships (utilizing the doctor's former mode of participation). (26)

(6) Pertinent communication between members through symbolic representation of dependent aspect of their interpersonal relations. (27)

(7) Doctor simultaneously participated on indirect, symbolized and direct ego levels of relationship. (In effect the doctor talked the patients' language, from society's point of view.) (28)

(8) Wish-fulfilling flight by mother and daughter subgroups, through travel fantasies, with indirect and symbolic commentary on this by patients. (29)

B. Appearance of Mothers' Direct Feelings (as a subgroup). (Inadequacy and Guilt.)

(1) Differences within mothers' subgroup over mothering, with expression by mothers of range of attitudes about guilt and some identification with

the daughters, and vague recrimination by their daughters. (30, 31, 32, 33)

(2) Personal exposition by mothers of their own dependent reactions in the past, with denial mechanisms prominent. (34)

(3) Attention by the mothers to denial by daughter and evidence of denial of the daughter in the present. (35)

(4) Denial by daughter of mother and of own identity as a girl, and counterdenial by mother. (36)

C. Mothers grappled with the provocative, dissident, abandoning trends in daughter and in themselves (as members of the mothers' subgroup).

(1) Coherent, yet differing approaches on an ego level among the mothers' subgroup to daughters' adherence to denial and autism. (37, 38, 39)

(2) Doctor guided group back to current ego relationships with daughter, with attention to aggressive intent of mothers. (41)

(3) Fragmentary interaction of mother and daughter about mother's giving in to another. (42)

(4) Struggle within mothers' subgroup between dependent and responsible ego approaches, with identification of self by representative mother with the latter. (43–47)

GROUP PSYCHOTHERAPY WITH MEMBERS OF FAMILIES

Parallel treatment of patients and their relatives in different groups has been going on at least since 1943. The early reports deal primarily with group process and do not make it clear how much was done with the relationship of patient and relative. Ross (6),* who worked with groups of relatives of psychotic patients, used the meetings to explain the nature of mental illness and to modify traumatic attitudes to patients. Fabian, Crampton and Holden (9), Gabriel and Halpern (10), and Bauer and Gurevitz (11)—all report on groups of parents meeting parallel with those of their children. The focus in all these groups is on the child, though the parents are given opportunity to talk about themselves. This point is made most clearly in the paper of Bauer and Gurevitz, who obtained permission from the children to relate their problems to the parents; thus, the parents knew some of what went on in the children's group, but the procedure was not reciprocal. This experiment was the closest to the one reported here; the difference between them is a major one because of the one-sided nature of the communication.

Placing relatives together in the same group is obviously doing more than increasing the size of the group; it introduces a change in the nature of the group by bringing into the group situation at the start the full-blown reciprocal tensions and attitudes which the two related persons have toward one an-

* Numbers in parentheses refer to "Bibliography on Group Psychotherapy with Members of Families." See pp. 236–237.

other. When a group of strangers are brought together in a therapy group, each brings his tensions and attitudes from the outside into it; but, although he may project on some other member of the group the role of the person toward whom he has these feelings, reciprocation is revealed gradually.

The essential differences between treating strangers in a group and treating related persons in a group may be broached by examining how each of these situations helps the group member with interpersonal problems outside of the group. A group of mothers of problem children, for example, may help individual members by dealing with problems which are more or less related to their problems with their children. Such may be the mother's need to keep up a front in front of her neighbors, her inability to act aggressively where situations require it, her problems in expressing negative feelings, problems about sex. As such problems are worked through in the group the mother may relax in general, and this relaxation may be reflected in a more tolerant and understanding attitude toward her child. In addition, while working through these problems she may have come to understand better what she was doing with her child and with insight modify her attitudes and behavior toward him. Change in the relationship between mother and child, if it occurs, is a by-product of the changes that have occurred in the mother in the group. This means that these changes in the mother must be of such degree either to be noticeable by the child, or to allow the mother to initiate a change in her relationship with the child.

When the mother and the sick child are present together in the same group, they bring with them all of the tensions, antagonisms and so forth which they habitually entertain toward one another. The mother is faced with her preoccupation with the relationship with the child, something she has habitually turned to, away from her difficulties with her neighbors or her own problems in the expression of feelings. There is an opportunity for her to work through some of this tendency. The issues which are creating difficulties between parent and child are immediately present and can therefore be subjected to examination by the doctor, the parent and the child, and by other members of the group. In this situation, both mother and child may own up to problems, feelings, experiences which had not been discussed before. The discussion itself may not seem to effect a change in the speaker, whereas hearing it may have a profound evident effect on the other person. In the presence of the doctor the mothers in this group admitted that they had similar problems of being depressed, confused, distraught. That is, they publicly admitted that they were not superior, and this admission must have had an effect on the patients whether or not the mothers' behavior remained superior.

Bowlby (7), in one case, after treating the parents and the child separately, brought them together. The child was emotionally disturbed, lazy and unco-operative. The first part of this session was spent on recrimination by each member of the family. Then the therapist brought out the techniques that each member of the family used, which irritated the others. This led the mother to divulge some of her own unhappy childhood experiences, and subsequently the tenor of the situation changed to one of attempting to find constructive ways of living together. The implication is that there was an immediate modification of the relationship between the parents and the child as a result of this session.

Dr. Samuel B. Hadden of Philadelphia has not at the time of this writing published anything on work with families in groups, but has reported to us something of his experiences. He brought together several families in a single group after treating parents and children separately. Although the experiment lasted for only two or three sessions, the members of the group got down to basic issues. For example, one family included a boy who had been acting out his hostility toward his father by predelinquent behavior. The father did not realize what the boy's feeling was, but was reacting with irritation to this behavior. In the group, the boy talked about his hatred for his father. The father immediately began to react to this, but before he could say anything the boy stopped him by adding, "Yes, Dad, and you hate Grandma and wish she were dead." The father's reaction then subsided and from then on the family situation began to improve. In view of the kind of material which emerged so quickly, it is not surprising that Dr. Hadden reports that the tensions and anxieties manifest in this group were very great as compared with those of other groups.

This example from Dr. Hadden's group illustrates the difference between helping relatives by working separately on their individual attitudes, and helping them by working out their difficulties directly with each other. (This is not meant to imply that this family would have been helped equally well without individual help as well as the group.) In this case, the son replaced his acting out of his hostility by actually verbalizing the hostility to the father; he forestalled his father's reaction and made his own feelings more understandable toward his father by pointing out that his father was like him in that he had analogous feelings toward his own mother. Presumably the presence of other group members inhibited a display of argumentative or hostile behavior and the realization that he was like his son made the father more understanding and accepting. The focus of the parent's attention shifted from reacting to the antisocial behavior to understanding the boy's feelings toward himself. Simultaneously as the boy was given the opportunity to express his feelings and have them accepted, his need for acting them out diminished.

In the group of schizophrenic women and their mothers studied here, the problem was more complicated. The doctor had no individual relationship with either the patients or their mothers; the difficulty in both cases was greatly intensified over the case just cited, for neither patient nor mother was ready to acknowledge feelings or talk about them. The first part of the therapeutic task was to create the possibility of their doing this, and only subsequently could there be a recognition and acceptance of the problems troubling them. Only after months of meetings, for example, did it become apparent that the mothers reacted to the patients' illness with the same anger and disapproval as the father of this boy showed toward the predelinquent behavior; and the patients, of course, were still farther away from being able to bring out directly the feeling which was being indirectly acted out in the illness.

Because the mothers and the patients were simultaneously present, the irritated behavior or attitude which each displayed toward the other was always potentially present. The focusing on the parent-child relationship, and on how their participation might be a reaction to one another enabled the members to move toward direct expression of the feelings hitherto expressed only through obscure and deviant behavior. Thus, the issues about which they were mutually concerned could eventually come into focus.

Because of the contrasting nature of the approaches to therapy, it is useful to compare the findings of this investigation with those of Peck, Rabinovitch, and Cramer (8), who treated the parents of schizophrenic children at Bellevue Hospital.

The parents in this experiment were treated in a group *without* the children, and the therapists were focusing on helping the parent, as opposed to the present experiment, which focused on helping the mother-daughter pair, together and as individuals.

Some similarities between the two groups are immediately apparent. In both experiments, the parents had extreme difficulty in accepting the child's condition as an illness, and in relinquishing the child to the hospital. Some of the effects of treatment are also similar: in both cases, there was a diminution of guilt, of stigma, increased ability to give up the sick child, general diminution of tension in the home.

There are some immediately apparent differences: the schizophrenic children in the Bellevue group had not been sick as long and had not yet been hospitalized. One may conjecture that the illness of the child had not affected the mothers as deeply in these cases, and that it was therefore easier to modify the mothers. In the St. Elizabeths group, where the patients had been hospitalized for years, the mothers themselves spoke in group meetings of how they had developed "pachydermatous shells" which made them less accessible, and which they reported were beginning to dissolve after about a year of meetings.

The therapist's focus was the reverse in the two groups: at Bellevue the focus was on helping the parents by relieving them of guilt and responsibility for the illness of the child. In the group reported here, the focus was on helping both the patients and the mothers by modifying their relationship with each other. When the mothers at St. Elizabeths blamed the illness on physical causes, this was in time considered as resistance to the examination of the relationship rather than as reality.

In view of these very major differences in the two groups, the similarities in the results are all the more striking. Without its being the initial intent of the doctor at St. Elizabeths to alleviate the anxiety, guilt or tension of the mother in other relationships, this nevertheless occurred. Conversely, the Bellevue group found that where tension in the home and the parents' anxiety diminished, the relationship with the sick child improved. The report on the Bellevue group, however, says nothing about change in the patients' condition, and it leaves the impression that it was not affected by the group treatment.

One interesting difference may be related to the therapist's focus, that is, in the Bellevue group the parents emphasized the excessive nature of the emotional demands made by the patients. "They make a terrible drain on your love and give so little in return." The St. Elizabeths group, on the other hand, revealed in the course of treatment the mothers' own great emotional dependence on the patients.

An important question remains unanswered as a result of this comparison—what essential difference between the two groups can be attributed to treating the mothers and patients jointly. With respect to this, it may be significant that the Bellevue doctors report that the parents benefited most in those cases where both parents attended the group. This may mean that where a relationship can be worked on by two parties to it, better results are obtained.

BIBLIOGRAPHY ON GROUP PSYCHOTHERAPY WITH MEMBERS OF FAMILIES

1. Amster, Fannie, "Collective Psychotherapy of Mothers of Emotionally Disturbed Children," *Am. J. Orthopsychiatry,* January, 1944.
2. Durkin, Helen E., Glatzer, Henrietta and Hirsch, Jeannette S., "Therapy of Mothers in Groups," *Am. J. Orthopsychiatry,* January, 1944.
3. Kolodney, Etta, "Treatment of Mothers in Groups as a Supplement to Child Psychotherapy," *Mental Hygiene,* July, 1944.

4. Ackerman, Nathan W., "Some General Principles in the Use of Group Psychotherapy," in *Current Therapies in Personality Disorders,* ed. Bernard Glueck, New York, Grune & Stratton, 1946.

5. Donald M. Hamilton, "The Psychiatric Hospital as a Cultural Pattern," in *Current Therapies of Personality Disorders,* ed. Bernard Glueck, New York, Grune & Stratton, 1946.

6. Ross, W. D., "Group Psychotherapy with Psychotic Patients and Their Relatives," *Am. J. Psychiatry, 105:* 383–386, 1948.

6a. Ross, W. D., "Group psychotherapy with Patients' Relatives." *Am. J. Psychiatry, 104:* 623–626, 1948.

7. Bowlby, John, "The Study and Reduction of Group Tensions in the Family," *Human Relations, 2:* 123–128, 1949.

8. Peck, Harris B., Rabinovitch, Ralph D., and Cramer, Joseph B., "A Treatment Program for Parents of Schizophrenic Children," *Am. J. Orthopsychiatry, 19:* 592–598, 1949.

9. Fabian, Abraham A., Crampton, Jessie E., and Holden, Marjorie A., "Parallel Group Treatment of Pre-School Children and Their Mothers," *Int. J. Group Psychotherapy, 1:* 37–50, 1951.

10. Gabriel, Betty, and Halpert, Anita, "The Effect of Group Therapy for Mothers on Their Children," *Int. J. Group Psychotherapy, 2:* 159–171, 1952.

11. Bauer, Irving L. and Gurevitz, Saul, "Group Therapy with Parents of Schizophrenic Children," *Int. J. Group Psychotherapy, 2:* 344–357, 1952.

BIBLIOGRAPHY OF THE VETERANS ADMINISTRATION GROUP PSYCHO-THERAPY RESEARCH PROJECT

1. Fearing, J. M. and MacGregor, R. Analysis of the group process in the therapeutic session. *International Journal of Group Psychotherapy, 1*: 126–129, 1951.
2. Frank, J. D. Group psychotherapy in relation to research. *Group Psychotherapy, 3*: 197–203, 1950.
3. Frank, J. D. Some problems of research in group psychotherapy. *International Journal of Group Psychotherapy, 1*: 78–81, 1951.
4. Frank, J. D. Group psychotherapy with chronic hospitalized schizophrenics. In E. B. Brody and F. C. Redlich (eds.), *Psychotherapy with Schizophrenics: A Symposium*. New York: International Universities Press, 1952, pp. 216–230.
5. Frank, J. D. The effects of interpatient and group influences in a general hospital. *International Journal of Group Psychotherapy, 2*: 127–138, 1952.
6. Frank, J. D. Group methods in psychotherapy. *Journal of Social Issues, 2*: 35–44, 1952.
7. Frank, J. D. Areas of research in group psychotherapy. (Chapter in annual volume published by Association for Research in Nervous and Mental Diseases. In press.)
8. Frank, J. D. and Ascher, E. Corrective emotional experiences in group therapy. *American Journal of Psychiatry, 108*: 126–131, 1951.
9. Frank, J. D., Ascher, E., Margolin, J. B., Nash, Helen, Stone, A. R., and Varon, Edith J., Behavioral patterns in early meet-

ings of therapeutic groups. *American Journal of Psychiatry, 108*: 771–778, 1952.

10. Frank, J. D., Margolin, J. B., Nash, Helen T., Stone, A. R., Varon, Edith, and Ascher, E. Two behavior patterns in therapeutic groups and their apparent motivation. *Human Relations, 5*: 289–317, 1952.

11. Maas, H. S., and Varon, Edith. The caseworker in clinical and sociopsychological research. *Social Service Review, 23*: 302–314, 1949.

12. Maas, H. S., Varon, Edith, and Rosenthal, D. A technique for studying the social behavior of schizophrenics. *Journal of Abnormal and Social Psychology, 46*: 119–123, 1951.

13. Margolin, J. B. The use of an interaction matrix to validate patterns of group behavior. *Human Relations, 5:* 407–416, 1952.

14. McDonald, E. The masking function of self-revelation in group therapy. *International Journal of Group Psychotherapy, 1*: 59–63, 1951.

15. Nash, Helen T., Margolin, J. B., and MacGregor, R. A functional approach to interpretation of the Rorschach. *Journal of General Psychology* (in press).

16. Nash, Helen T. and Stone, A. R. Collaboration of therapist and observer in guiding group psychotherapy. *Group Psychotherapy, 4*: 85–92, 1951.

17. Powdermaker, Florence. Concepts found useful in treatment of schizoid and ambulatory schizophrenic patients. *Psychiatry, 15:* 61–72, 1952.

17a. Powdermaker, Florence and Frank, J. D. Group psychotherapy with neurotics. *American Journal of Psychiatry, 105:* 449–455, 1948.

18. Powdermaker, Florence and Frank, J. D. *Group Psychotherapy: Studies in Methodology of Research and Therapy.* Cambridge: Harvard University Press, 1953.

19. Powell, J. W., Stone, A. R., and Frank, J. D. Group reading and group therapy: A concurrent test. *Psychiatry, 15*: 33–51, 1952.

20. Varon, Edith. Localizing a patient's difficulties through a sys-

tematic study of his interpersonal relationships. *Journal of Psychiatric Social Work, 20*: 17–21, 1950.

21. Varon, Edith. Recurrent phenomena in group psychotherapy. *International Journal of Group Psychotherapy, 3*: 49–58, 1953.

22. Varon, Edith and Maas, H. S. Evaluating social adjustment through a systematic study of interpersonal relationships. *Journal of Psychiatric Social Work, 21*: 3–12, 1951.